SUPER

A MEMOIR

J.J. MORRIS WITH JON COFFEY

Published by Double Shot Publishing, an independent publisher.

ISBN: 978-1-7330358-1-1
eBook ISBN: 978-1-7330358-0-4

Printed in the United States of America on acid-free paper

Book design by Brianna Coffey

To Ryan and Eric
and all the boys becoming men.

The names of persons and locations referred to in this work have been altered to maintain the privacy and safety of the individuals involved.

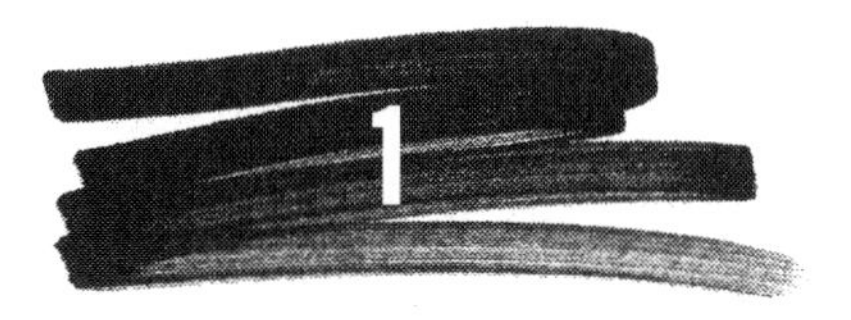

I first suspected I was different from everyone else in the world two weeks before the start of my junior year of high school.

I was sixteen.

It was an early-August morning in Oak Hill, Michigan, and there was a golden haze that drenched the world in warm, hopeful tones. A wispy shroud of fog hung low in the air as Thomas Winters, my best friend since I can remember, and I, walked out of the locker room in our cleats, crunching across the small asphalt parking lot at the back of our high school.

"Are you ready for this, JJ?" he asked.

"I guess we'll find out."

He sighed. "I guess we will."

On the practice field before us, between the fog and backdrop of angular light from over the tree line, I could just make out the fuzzy shapes of some of my peers, adorned in pads, huddled in groups, with some already donning shiny white football helmets. Others held their headgear at their sides or had it on the ground near their feet. A few of the guys were trying to do some stretching on their own on the damp grass. There was a soft buzz in the air—nervous conversation and murmurs about what kind of torturous feats would be asked of us in the coming hours.

The first week of football practice was both the most exciting and most nerve-wracking thing in my life up to that point. It was five straight days of grueling two-a-days where the coaches would examine every speck of our football ability. Each year I would prepare myself for the worst, while simultaneously hoping the coaches would be impressed with what I had to offer. On Friday, Thomas and I, and the rest of the hopeful juniors would wait nervously to see where our names had been printed on one of two pieces of white paper that would be tacked to the cork board in the locker room. The seniors would all be listed in italics on the paper labeled "Varsity." Next to every name would be the abbreviation of the position they played along with a number that indicated them as a starter or a second or third string player. The second sheet of paper was structured the same way, but read "JV" at the top of the page. To be listed as a varsity starter as a junior, while somewhat rare at Oak Hill, was not a far stretch of the imagination. It earned you immediate respect just to be on the team, even as a senior.

Coach Bill Haines, a history teacher who served as the Oak Hill High School track and field head coach and offensive coordinator on the varsity football team, blew his whistle and gathered us together. I remember his voice cracking as he yelled for everyone to get in lines. He'd coached the freshmen team the year before when Coach McNamara left to take a job in Illinois in the middle of the season, but I had known Coach Haines since the day Mrs. Sandy had gotten sick, and he'd filled in as the teacher of my Sunday school class when I was six years old. He told us the story of Samson. He was just getting to the good part, after Samson's eyes get gouged out, when someone's mom came in and started to make a scene. Evidently, he was supposed to be teaching us about Noah's ark and how the animals went two-by-two but had called an audible at the last minute in favor of what he called "a story little boys needed to hear." The decision wound up costing him an earful from a bunch of angry parents and one of the deacons in the hallway. I thought his story was clearly the better of the two and couldn't understand why they wouldn't let him at least tell us the ending.

In the time I'd known him, Coach Haines had always worn thick glasses that made his eyes look bigger than they were, but as I stood on the practice field, I realized how much older he looked than that day at church. The dark hair beneath his baseball cap was peppered with grey, and the lines in his cheeks and around his eyes had deepened. He was taking us through warm-ups, swinging a silver whistle in circles by its lanyard, occasionally stopping to ask us about our summers. His calm demeanor gave me the impression the whole thing was going to be pretty laid back, but the knots in my stomach refused to believe. I had just forced myself to take a deep, calming breath when I saw two big shadows sprawl out across the grass in front of my outstretched legs.

"Listen up greenhorns," one of the men barked. It was Brian Briggs, head coach of the Oak Hill varsity football team. He was in his early forties, short, compact, muscly, and beginning to show minor signs of a beer belly. Back in the day, he had been a standout high school running back from Flint, but a knee injury cut his freshman year of college ball short and required a surgery that ended his playing career. He graduated with a degree in theater, and there were rumors that he had moved to Hollywood for a while before he started coaching. By the time I got to try out for the varsity team, Briggs had been a high school football coach in some capacity for nearly fifteen years, though this was only his third season as a head coach. He was eager to prove himself and earn respect, and he was well-liked because of his big personality. Traces of his schooling as an actor showed themselves in recurring roles at football practice, in his classroom, and especially during his pregame speeches in the locker room. When I met him, he'd already enjoyed moderate success as a football coach, and with his build that hinted at his former athleticism and his exaggerated surly disposition, he came across as an intimidating guy when he wasn't reciting lines from Shakespeare. Everyone, including non-football students and parents, simply called him "Briggs."

At this moment, the energetic head coach stood next to a man I'd never seen before. The man was suited up in full football pads.

"This is Marcus Day," Briggs said, as he peered around the crowd through his shiny aviator glasses that were shaded under a maroon baseball cap. "He's from Texas. Played varsity ball down there with the big boys, as a freshman. He said they called him 'Hacksaw,' down there."

I know, I know! I swear I'm not making this stuff up. This kid was a mammoth, and looked as though he could grow a full beard at a moment's notice; a hulking mass of a tenth grader. And he seriously went by the name Hacksaw. I didn't know whether to laugh or cry.

I thought about the one hundred and forty pounds that made up my wiry frame, and what might happen to it against the force of the beast standing in front of me.

Briggs informed us that Hacksaw would almost certainly be playing on the varsity squad, but since all of us would be spending a lot of time together competing over the following days, he wanted to formally introduce us, before we were informally introduced. We were all a little less eager to get up from doing our stretches after that.

The week of practices moved along and everything was going fairly well. Thomas was working out with the quarterbacks and had thrown a couple of nice passes. Hacksaw had been garnering the praise of the coaches at most every opportunity, tackling with near-perfect form, outrunning everyone on the team during conditioning drills, and even catching passes. I had managed not to puke despite the gauntlet of sprints, and avoided looking like a chump up to that point, which felt like an accomplishment.

But then came the last session on Thursday afternoon, and the thing my teenage self dreaded more than anything else—Bull in the Ring.

It was a "game" designed to test toughness, instinct, and probably has been used in scientific papers as evidence of the trauma suffered by football players. But I digress. Basically, the game was comprised of all the participants forming a wide circle around one guy, with everyone facing in toward the single player. The coaches would walk behind all of the players, and if you felt a slap on your shoulder pads that was your cue to sprint as fast as you could and ferociously tackle the player in the middle of the circle. The sneakier you were, and more off-guard you caught him the better. Once that was over, you became the prey, and someone would come and try to take you out. Really, Bull in the Ring weeded out the fakers. And that was why it made me cringe to even think about it. I feared I would be weeded out and cast aside. The game never failed to do its job, and I had resigned myself to the idea that one day I would be exposed for the pretender I really was.

Hoping that day wasn't this day, I stood somewhere in that circle of destruction, watching guys get pummeled. A senior saw a junior coming and flipped him over his shoulders. A few moments later a fellow junior tried a similar maneuver, but another senior lowered his shoulder and crumpled the kid into a heap, bringing out the wild, primal screams of the crowd of players and coaches.

Thomas made it into the middle of the circle after getting a fortunate shot at a smaller player. But his luck ran out, as one of the assistant coaches slapped Hacksaw's helmet. With his tenacity about to be fully unveiled at last, Hacksaw leapt into action, shooting out of his position, growling. He reached Thomas in a flash, and dove with his feet leaving the ground. It felt like time was going half the normal speed, and I thought my heart was slowing to a stop as Hacksaw's shoulder connected with Thomas, dispersing the crunching sound of plastic colliding at high speeds. Thomas flew a few feet through the air, which isn't much of an exaggeration. His arms flailed like one of those inflatable things at car dealerships before he landed in a heap. It was impressive and horrifying at the same time. Everyone around the circle was cheering wildly in awe. Thomas rolled to his side and slowly began to gather strength enough to try to stand. He shook his head a few times as he braced himself on the grass with his arm. And then I got a dreadful feeling—I was next.

The weight of a heavy arm pressed onto my shoulder pads. The arm wrapped around my exposed neck between my helmet and pads. I could feel the sweat and the hair as he pulled me toward his face. It was Briggs.

"Rootin' for ya, kid," he said with a twisted grin. He spit, and then I felt the smack of his hand on the back of my helmet, directing me toward the center of the ring.

Stumbling forward, I turned my head to get my bearings, only to see Hacksaw already barreling toward me screaming with all the rage he could muster. Everyone was yelling and I could feel the impending moment—almost see it unfolding. I recovered from my misstep, planted my foot in the ground, lowered my head and shoulders, and took a deep breath. I shut my eyes as if I were about to jump into a cold swimming pool, and leaned in, all of my weight pointed toward the barreling bull.

I felt the coolness of his helmet on my arm just below my shoulder pad a split second before I heard the cracking thud of our pads hitting. With my eyes still shut, I could feel my body falling backwards, and imagined Hacksaw soaring over the top of me as my body became parallel to the ground.

But I didn't hit the ground, and the volume of the crowd surrounding us rose to a thundering roar.

I opened my eyes and felt as though I had just misjudged the number of steps in a flight of stairs. I nearly fell onto my hands and knees. I was standing. I gasped for breath.

Hacksaw was several yards away from me lying on his back. His arms and legs were sprawled in varying directions and his helmet had dozens of tiny cracks protruding from the point of impact like some tiny meteor had crash landed onto his head.

Players were jumping up and down in excitement, fueled by unbridled adrenaline. I looked around and my eyes met Thomas's. His mouth gaped as he stared at me—a dumbfounded expression in his eyes. Thomas had never looked at me like that, and I felt for a moment that perhaps I had done something wrong. I looked down at my hands, checking to see if anything was broken. I looked down at my shoulder and arm that took the blow, and then found myself looking over my shoulder. Briggs was standing with his hands on his knees in the position he always assumed on the sidelines during games. And for maybe the only time that I've known him, he looked speechless as he glanced back and forth between the unmoving form of Hacksaw and me.

My freshman and sophomore years hadn't gone as I had hoped they might when I left the halls of junior high behind. They weren't traumatic. They weren't disasters. They weren't anything, and that was the problem.

My classes weren't nearly as hard as all the kids older than me made them out to be. Being in high school had turned out to be uneventful. I was figuring out that I wasn't a standout athlete, or a genius, or a rockstar or a comedian or any other thing a teenager might aspire to be. Thomas and I stuck together, of course, but we didn't roll with any of the usual cliques—mainly because I couldn't figure out what clique I was supposed to be in. Thomas fit the bill for at least a few. He was the kind of guy that always had something entertaining to say, never studied for a test, and always ended up with an A. His dad always said Thomas was destined to either be a doctor or a circus clown. I always guessed that maybe the reason he was so hesitant to align himself with one of the social groups at school was because he wasn't sure if they'd take both of us, but I wasn't ever sure that was the reason. He always said it was because he didn't want to box himself in. "That's a four-year commitment. I want to keep my options open."

We were our own group we decided—us and a few others. But we weren't that happy about it. Our lunch table had expanded from just the two of us to a whopping six by the school year's end, but that was more to do with the fact that our table was seen as more of a catch-all than a specific group. We were a group, we just had no rules, no requirements, no name, and no distinguishable features.

We disappeared into the crowd, like the rest of my first two years at Oak Hill High.

If my high school career had been a flavor, it would've been vanilla.

After eight semesters in the big leagues, I had nothing to show for it—no awards, no reputation, and no girlfriend.

So I'd be lying if I said it didn't feel really good to walk around at football practice after what everyone was calling "the hit." I felt like I had grown three inches and walked around with the best posture I think I ever had. Even the senior guys looked a little nervous around me. Briggs seemed to say, "Helluva hit, kid" every time he looked at me.

Before he posted the team rosters and depth charts, Briggs pulled me into his sweaty office that you had to enter through the boys' locker rooms, and said he wanted me to skip the JV team and practice with varsity to begin the year.

"I wasn't planning on that, ya know?" he said. "But I've never seen anything like that hit. I've been around football for decades and I've never seen a cocky son-of-a-bitch monster get an ass-kicking like that. And if there's more of that in there (here he pointed at me dramatically), I want to know."

It's weird, you know, because I was pretty much unknown up to that point in my life. I mean, yes, I had friends at school and my teachers seemed to like me just fine. But I simply blended in with everything. I was just another one of the guys that hung around. I played sports, but I wasn't the star on any team. I was just there. I just existed. Or at least that's what everyone saw.

I had this really bad habit of being painfully shy throughout elementary school and junior high. There were always a hundred things I thought to say, or wanted to do, but felt terrified to act on any of them. I never wanted to put out the wrong vibe, or do something that might cause me to be remembered as That Guy. At that time in my life, That Guy was the worst thing you could be. I didn't want to be remembered as that guy who always said the wrong thing in class, so I never said anything, except for when the teacher would call on me and make me answer a question. I didn't want to be known as that guy who got rejected by the girl he had a crush on, so I never told anyone who that was, and certainly never said anything to the girl. I never wanted to be that guy whose family was disappointed in him, so I got Bs and Cs because I knew I could always get a B or a C. Getting an A meant a higher standard I might not always live up to.

Inside, I was completely different. I had ambition and wanted admiration. I was actually quite competitive, and a bit of a showman. But my fears always told the showman to go away. Even when I finally reached high school and my crippling fear started to level off, I still couldn't shake the paralyzing feeling that a mistake might make me stand out too much, and for all the wrong reasons.

After the hit at practice I was That Guy—that guy who pummeled the Hacksaw. I remember hearing some kid say something like, "Hacksaw was going to get a full-ride scholarship to play in college, but I bet he won't ever even play football again." I always laughed a little bit when I heard stuff like that. I knew I hadn't short-circuited the Hacksaw for good. If anything, I probably made him madder and more ferocious than he already was.

But I found that walking around being That Guy wasn't so bad. At least, it wasn't so bad if That Guy was cool. In this case he was.

I walked into high school on the first day of my junior year with newfound confidence in every stride. I never imagined that people would actually recognize me. And it wasn't just the football guys. Two senior girls came up to me and said they'd heard about the hit and me making varsity. I was so taken off guard that I don't think I said a word to them. They just laughed and went on their way. My life was changing.

The first class of my junior year at Oak Hill High School was with Mr. Lawrence in Pre-Calculus. I was a little stunned at the number of homework assignments and tests he listed on the syllabus. I didn't remember anywhere near that volume during Algebra II the year before. But for the first time in my life I was ecstatic to be at school.

The bell rang and everyone got up to go to their next class. I got held up talking to a couple of guys hanging around Thomas, who had made the JV team as the clear favorite for starting quarterback, and heard the warning bell ring. I hurried off to my locker as everyone else started clearing out. The halls were nearly empty by the time I reached locker 226. I twisted the combination lock, settled it at 8, twisted the knob completely to the right twice, settling on 5, and then nudged it over a few notches to 12. The lock popped open and I hurried to open the door as quickly as I could.

Did you know that lockers are connected? As in, they come in sets. I'd never paid much attention to the construction of lockers, but when I went to open my locker in a rush, I ripped the entire locker section off the wall. It creaked and squealed the way metal does when it gets dragged across linoleum a couple of inches. It felt like I had barely pulled on the door. I looked around in horror to see if there was a teacher ready to expel me. Fortunately, there weren't any teachers, but there was a girl with golden hair—another junior—standing in the middle of the hallway apparently having waited until the last second to get to class. I recognized her from the table of popular girls in the cafeteria. We'd gone to school together for several years, but I couldn't recall any time where we'd ever spoken to each other. She was staring at me.

"What did you do?" she asked.

I had no answer besides the truth.

"I tried to open my locker." We stood there looking at each other and the lockers for a couple of long moments. Neither of us knew what to do or say. I wanted to laugh, but I was afraid she'd think I had done it intentionally… somehow.

"This place must be falling apart," she said.

A teacher yelled for us to get to class from somewhere down the hall, and we heard his door slam shut in annoyance.

The girl hurried off to her next class, which happened to be the same direction I was headed. I caught up to her and we were nearly moving along at a run together as we turned around a corner and toward a hallway with more doors. She said, "bye," and veered off to knock on the door we were passing. I looked down at my class schedule and realized I was supposed to be there as well.

"Sneaking off together already?" the young-ish woman who answered the door said. She was wearing a black pencil skirt and had her hair up in a neat bun. Teacher. It was Ms. Henry. Unknowingly, she was a frequent subject of many conversations and dirty jokes in the boys' locker room. As she stood before me, I remembered how Thomas had been a little disheartened when he saw that I had Henry for English Lit. & Humanities and that he had the old crotchety Mr. Spells instead.

Ms. Henry maintained a stern look until she saw that we were clueless to her attempt at a joke, and then quickly smiled and welcomed us into the class. I followed the blonde girl into the room and we took the two empty seats nearest the whiteboard. Ms. Henry's high heels clicked all the way up to the front of the room where she started scribbling next to some words already written there and said, "Now, as I was saying…"

I felt a tap on my arm, and looked to my right to see the blonde girl leaned over with her fist extended to me, offering me something.

"You dropped this," she whispered.

"Oh, thanks," I whispered back. I was really trying to play it cool, but I didn't think I'd dropped anything. I held out my hand and she placed a small folded piece of paper onto my palm. I was a bit confused. I knew I hadn't dropped that.

I rested my arms on the desk and tried to subtly unfold the paper and read the words written in big, neat blue letters.

Hi!

-Elle

Elaine Vance ran with the popular crowd at school. Her family had moved to Oak Hill the summer between junior high and high school. But even though she was just the new girl, it took her no time to make friends with all the right people. She was known and adored by many of the upperclassmen because her brother, Robby, was a senior and played on the basketball, baseball, and football teams. She made the varsity cheerleading squad that year, and between that, her natural charm, her acceptance by the juniors and seniors, and the fact that she was really cute, she had been deemed cool by the rest of the school—a label that had easily carried over to our junior year. Everyone called her, "Elle."

3

Around the time the Vances moved to town, Thomas and I were both 14 and had just started testing the waters of being friends with girls. I had seen the way girls looked at their boyfriends with a sort of dreamy, satisfied look and it made me want someone to look at me like that. But, of course, I couldn't tell all of that to Thomas.

The first girl we became friends with was Coach Haines's daughter whom we had both known since kindergarten. Her name was Charlie. Mostly, we just hung out with her at church since there weren't very many people our age there. But then, once the school year started, we all sat by each other in World History. We talked a lot, laughed a lot, and got shushed a lot by Mr. Dixon. It was great, especially after that brutal stretch at the end of elementary that lasts well into junior high, where boys are too afraid to talk to anyone that isn't another boy or a teacher, and girls treat their male classmates as if they all carry a highly contagious disease.

Charlie was cool. She didn't seem to act like the other girls. Her dad coached football. She appeared to enjoy being around us. And she thought we were funny. We liked that just fine. We stayed friends through the rest of that school year and throughout our sophomore year as well.

When we came back to school as juniors, neither Thomas or I had seen much of Charlie since we all went and got ice cream after the final bell of tenth grade. We'd all been busy over the summer. Thomas and I with football, keeping me almost entirely, and Thomas mostly, from church, and Charlie visiting her family out in California before heading out on a mission trip with the church to Jamaica.

I was walking up to the front doors of OHHS when I saw Charlie again. Except I didn't know it was Charlie.

It wasn't until later, when Thomas described what she was wearing, and that she looked "different" (he said this with a smirk) that I understood who she was. Charlie had grown up, matured, come into her own, whatever you want to call it. I almost couldn't find words to say to her when we finally got the chance to talk at lunch.

"I heard about the football team," she said, and hugged me. She smelled wonderful. Some kind of perfume, or maybe just some quality shampoo. I don't know. And again, I was still getting used to the idea of being friends with girls at this point. I didn't know they could smell like that.

"Yeah our little JJ is growing up," Thomas said.

"Shut up," I said. Thomas laughed.

"No, but really," Charlie insisted. "That's so awesome. I'm so happy for you. Did you play much last year?"

"Well..." I had no idea what to say.

"JJ's just a man, that's all," Thomas said. He was mimicking the pride that old dads have when they talk about their sons in peewee sports. "Taught him everything I know."

"Shut up, man," I said. We all laughed.

"No, but for real," Thomas said. "You should've seen the hit— "

The bell rang, signaling the end of lunch. We were all up and walking toward the door with the mass of other students.

"It was the craziest thing I've ever seen," Thomas raved. "And to think... JJ?! We've been friends our entire lives, and I never knew he had *that* in him!"

"Yeah," Charlie said. She was distracted and waving to someone walking down the hall toward us. "I heard about it."

Thomas shot me a wary glance.

"Have you guys met my boyfriend?" Charlie asked.

Out of all the guys in our school, somewhere around seven

hundred guys to choose from, and she had to date him. It was Hacksaw.

Because of their budding romance and intriguing social statures, Charlie Haines and Marcus "Hacksaw" Day, the new football kid from Texas, were elevated to the stratosphere of the popular crowd. I didn't take Charlie for the political type, but I wasn't one to put it past her either. She saw the opportunity to move up, and she took it. Hacksaw was fast friends with all the other jocks. He fit right in. They worked out together, ate mountains of food together, and all stood around talking about football together while their girlfriends fawned all over them. Seeing Charlie fawn over anyone other than Thomas or me made me nauseous. Thomas too, although I don't want to put words in his mouth, or feelings in his stomach.

Despite the change, Charlie was trying to stay friends with us. She still sat with us because she had a different lunch hour than Hacksaw or their other friends, and Hacksaw didn't seem to say much about it, but things weren't nearly the same as they had been before.

Within the first weeks of the school year, she invited us to come hang out with some of her new friends at a bonfire that Josh Williams, a senior varsity wide receiver, was hosting.

"Come on, you should come," Charlie pleaded after seeing my hesitation.

"I don't know, I don't really like bonfires," I said. It was a lie. Bonfires are great. S'mores, fire... what's not to like? The real reason was because being around Charlie with Hacksaw didn't feel right. I always felt like the third wheel, even if Thomas was with us too.

"We're not cool enough for them," Thomas said.

Charlie looked a little wounded. But she wasn't ready to give up. "I think you guys are cool. And, hey, you never know, you might find a girlfriend or something. Just come."

"Girlfriend?" Thomas said. He chuckled as he reached up and scratched the back of his head, feigning an attempt to brush her off.

"Yeah," she said. She moved in like a shark smelling blood in the water. "There's a bunch of people without significant others that are going to be there. My friend and her boyfriend just broke up. JJ, you probably know. She said she talked to you the other day."

"Who?" I said. But I knew.

"Elle."

4

The first football game of the season was on the Friday of the first week of school.

I was nervous as heck.

Practice had been going well enough for someone who was realizing he didn't actually know that much about football. I was quick to comprehend that I was in over my head when it came to playbooks, formations, gap assignments, defensive schemes, zone or man coverage, pre-snap adjustments—you know, the whole nine yards. But I was keeping up enough to secure the spot Briggs had given me. Most of the time, I had no idea of the specifics of where on the field I was supposed to be, or the complexities of what exactly it was I was supposed to be doing, but I was discovering that I was able to run much faster than I ever could and that was allowing me to recover from the numerous mental mistakes I made, much to the chagrin of the coaching staff.

That was why they decided to put me at safety. If you don't know, a safety in football is the last line of defense when a team is playing defense. There are many nuances to the position, but basically you stand as far away from the other team as you can without looking like you're completely out of the play and make sure no one scores. If someone tries to throw a deep pass to a receiver, the safety runs over to either make sure he doesn't catch it or make the tackle if he does.

If a running back breaks through the defensive line, and gets past the linebackers, it's up to the safety to bring him down. If everyone else forgets to tie their shoes on a play, the safety comes in to clean up the mess. So there you go. Safety valve. The underappreciated garbage man of the football world, cruising around the field cleaning up everyone else's mistakes.

It was much too obvious that I didn't know what I was doing for me to actually earn a starting spot, plus Austin Marks was a senior that had played defensive back on varsity for two years. But the coaches always said they liked my "hustle" and on more than one occasion I heard Briggs say, "Now there's a boy who don't quit."

A few weeks prior to the first Friday night game, we had gone through the time-honored tradition of being assigned our jersey numbers. It always seemed like a sacred ritual. Briggs would walk around the locker room handing out jerseys. A lot of guys would make it a point to tell him what number they wanted. Sometimes, especially if they were a good player, he would give them that number. But still, it was up to him. He would always start with the seniors and work his way through each class in descending order. Hacksaw and I were some of the only non-seniors on varsity, and by the time Briggs got to us, we knew there were few "good" numbers left—which is as arbitrary as it sounds. I don't even really know why numbers are a big deal, but as a high school kid, the whole thing felt like a really big deal.

There was a locker adorned with a piece of blue painter's tape with "MORRIS #47" scribbled in black marker, in front of me. By my estimation, forty-seven didn't mean a thing.

I sat in the locker room under the old brick grandstand of Henderson Field, where the Oak Hill Acorns played all their home football and soccer games. Yes, that is legitimately what we were called. The Acorns. Our principal, Mr. Cook, was kind of a quirky and yet intimidating guy in his late fifties, but he loved the Acorn thing, and at pep assemblies and graduations he always used to say, "The best thing about an acorn is its potential. A tiny little seed doesn't start off as much. It can get eaten or crushed, and forgotten. But if it makes it, if it perseveres through all the trials and hardships and is given the right care and opportunity to grow, it can become something extraordinary." And everyone would be completely drawn in and quiet, and then he'd always get them with something like: "But listen to me ramble on. That probably sounds nuts to all of you," and the people would laugh.

I wasn't in the starting lineup, but I got to run out of the tunnel donning the red and gold uniform of the Oak Hill Acorns with the rest of the team after the PA announcer had announced the starting lineup, finishing with, "and the rest of the Fightin' Acorns," to the roaring cheers of what felt like a pro stadium full of fans. In reality, I think average attendance was a little over 1,000 people on Friday nights in Oak Hill. There may have been a few more than usual that night because we were playing the Carrasco Pioneers, the school in the next town over from us, and it was the first game of the year. Since it was the tail end of summertime in Michigan, there was still a hint of blue in the sky overhead when the game started.

There was a constant buzz from the swarming masses, finding their seats and catching up with old friends in the home stands. It felt surreal to be on the field with all of these people here to watch, granted I knew they weren't there to watch me. I spotted my mom sitting with a few of the other moms in the crowd about a third of the way up. On the far end of the home-side seating was a standing mass of youthful fans wearing yellow-gold T-shirts emblazoned with the phrase "Go Nuts!"—the student section. Immediately, I saw Thomas waving in my direction. Charlie stood in front of Thomas wearing an oversized white shirt with a big red "33" on the front and sleeves and she saw me looking their way and waved as well. As I looked closer, dotted amongst the students adorned in yellow were many other girls donning the white uniforms with red numbers (the ones we wore when we played outside of Oak Hill) of their presumed boyfriends.

I returned them both a wave of acknowledgment and turned my

attention back to the field.

I felt minimal jitters after the national anthem, and even those had disappeared by the time we were losing 23-0 at the end of the first quarter and everyone wearing metallic gold and black were raucously celebrating in the visitors' bleachers.

By the time halftime rolled around, the sun had set, the stadium lights were on, and it was 35-0. The Pioneers were getting the best of us, and we all knew they wouldn't soon let us forget it if the score held.

We had to kick the ball off starting the second half and Briggs signaled to put me in the game.

I strapped on my red helmet and trotted out onto the field with a still immaculately clean jersey.

Kevin Parson kicked the ball and it soared down the field to the other end where one of the opposing team's players, wearing a white jersey with a black "5" on it, caught it and started to run toward us. I had started jogging toward the play without even realizing it. By the time he was getting near me, it felt like everyone was moving slow. As the runner wiggled in his stride to move past me and another tackler, I saw the ball clearly exposed in his left arm. I reached out and wildly swung my arm toward the slick brown textured surface. My arm collided with him and I felt him scramble to try to cover up his precious cargo as he, and I, and a bunch of other players, fell to the grass.

But the play wasn't over and the crowd roared louder. The ball was bouncing away from us a few yards over, and a herd of grunting football players were leaping toward it as a pile of bodies formed where there had just been a ball laying in a patch of green grass. I heard the loud shrieking whistle of a referee running past me to get to the mass of people writhing on top of where a ball was supposed to be.

I unbuckled my chinstrap and stood to watch. A black and white striped shirt emerged from the other side of the pile and the middle-aged man wearing it stood tall, gesturing toward the end zone of the receiving team. The Acorns had the ball!

My teammates all ran, jumping and punching the air and screaming things like, "LET'S GO!" as they returned to our sideline. I saw Briggs and jogged toward him. He smacked my shoulder pad and kind of pulled me past him, as he shouted in his most guttural tone, "Jacobs! Way to knock it free!" He embraced the player behind me, who failed to mention that it wasn't him who knocked the ball free.

I strolled toward the sideline, tearing my helmet from my head. A coach rose to his feet in front of me, looking concerned over my shoulder.

I turned and saw an ambulance driving out onto the field. I saw a black "5" on a white sleeve between the legs of a group of coaches, players, and trainers from the other team. A man and woman jumped out of the ambulance, opened its back doors and started to unload a stretcher.

A referee jogged over, and I moved closer to the field to hear what he would say.

"Looks like some broken ribs and a pretty messed up arm," he said. "Kid got lit up. This is going to take a couple of minutes."

"Heck-of-a hit, kid," Coach Haines said in a raspy voice after sidling up next to me. Because the freshmen typically played their games on Wednesdays, Haines acted as offensive coordinator during varsity games. He slapped my shoulder pad.

Haines walked over to Briggs and leaned in to say something through the din of the crowd and music playing from the PA system. Briggs's eyes darted in my direction. He gave me a seemingly knowing nod and tapped his fist to his chest twice and then pointed at me. I played the rest of the game on special teams, and even got in for a few plays near the end of the game on defense, but there was nothing to report after the fumble. We lost the game 42-12.

Briggs cracked a water cooler against a wall in the locker room during his post game speech.

5

I woke up early on the Saturday after that first football game before the sun came up with a pain in the arm I'd forced the fumble with, and the pain crept all the way up my arm and into my shoulder. *Some hit,* I thought.

My first game film session was at 9:00 a.m. and I wished I'd slept a bit longer. But, I felt well-rested and stomach-achingly hungry. It was strange for me to wake up before ten on a weekend let alone seven, but I got up and walked down the hall and into the kitchen. Our small house was quiet and grey at this hour. But the light above the stove was on, signaling that my mom had already left for work. I guessed that maybe she had woken me up when she shut the front door.

I remember the note I found on the counter by the sink. It read:

Hank called. Wanted to know about the game.
Breakfast in the freezer. Love you!

-Mom

So I picked up our silver cordless phone and dialed. The tone sang through the speaker, disturbing the quiet morning, and I quickly pressed the down arrow button on the side of the phone a few times. It started to ring a second time, but there were a few loud clicks and electronic scraping sounds.

"Hello?" It was Hank. "JJ?"

"Hey I saw you called," I said. "Going to work?"

"No I just got home. I'm on the overnight shift right now. That's why I wasn't there last night."

"Oh," I said. Neither of us said anything for a few seconds. I opened the freezer looking for the waffles.

"Well, how did it go?"

"It was all right," I said. "We got crushed." I saw the yellow box of waffles, but shut the freezer door without grabbing it.

"Well, did you get to play?"

"Yeah, but just on special teams," I said.

"That's fine. That's good. Better than not getting in."

"I guess." I opened the refrigerator door.

"How did it feel running out of that tunnel, huh?"

"It was okay."

"Just okay?" I remember the derisive chuckle he gave as he said it. "Weren't you nervous?"

"Uh... No, not really, I guess." I was leaned headfirst into the fridge.

"Well you just wait," he said. "It gets better."

"All right," I said. I pulled out a white Styrofoam take-out box and looked inside. Looked like some Jade House kung-pao chicken and chow mein leftovers from Thursday.

"When's the next home game?" Hank said. "I can't find that damn schedule you gave me."

"*Next* Friday," I said. I opened the silverware drawer and grabbed a fork. "But not next Friday, like, the *next* one. The one after the—"

"Okay, okay. I got you. I'm going to try to make that one, if Jerry doesn't make me work again."

"All right," I said as I loaded up my fork with noodles.

"Okay, well I'm gonna go sleep." I shoved the cold chow mein in my mouth.

I mumbled something, and then quickly chewed and tried to swallow the bite of food. "Hank," I said. "Have you ever broken someone's arm?"

Years before I ever went there, Hank was a standout wide receiver at Oak Hill High School, with scholarship offers from a couple of small in-state schools. He was a junior when the first letter arrived in his locker. He did well enough in school, he was the guy everyone wanted to be friends with, got invited to all the big parties, was adored throughout the town, and did especially well with the ladies. One night after an overtime win against Carrasco, Hank drove over to the big party where the football players and cool kids were going to be. It was at some farmhouse in the country, and there weren't any parents around. Someone had brought a few cases of beer and the good times were rolling. Sometime in the wee hours of the morning, Hank had gone back out to his car and was getting ready to leave when one of his football buddies threw open the screen door and yelled something to the effect of, "Hey Hank, Brown wants to make out with you."

Hank shrugged sheepishly and went back inside. Suzy Brown was a cheerleader, with a squeaky-clean reputation, and a make-you-blush smile. Every guy in school wanted a shot with her and most never got anywhere close. Ol' Hank couldn't pass up such an opportunity. He walked back in and kissed her without saying a word. Later, they left together in Hank's car.

It was maybe the most perfect night a pimply high school boy could dream up.

But two weeks later, they realized that perfect night had followed them. It was fun to be "the cutest couple" in school. It wasn't fun to be "the pregnant" couple.

Suzy delivered the news in the entranceway of the girls' bathroom in the freshman wing after Hank had noticed the wet streaks of mascara on her cheeks and tried to follow her in. Nothing was ever the same for either of them.

Although he tried to continue on in as normal of fashion as possible, Hank took a job at a local paper mill to start saving money for the baby before school let out. He'd never had a job before that. He had already stopped responding to college offer letters and vacated his role as captain and star centerfielder of the baseball team with six games left before the playoffs.

"Henry James, you're throwing your future away!" his dad had screamed at him.

Hank and Suzy graduated at Henderson Field on a sunny day in May at the end of the school year. They married at the Oak Hill courthouse a week later. The baby came in June.

Only Suzy's mom and dad came from either of their families to the hospital on the morning of June 19 to meet seven-pound, eight-ounce Jonah James Morris born at 5:37 a.m.

Grandma and Grandpa Brown have been sweet to me ever since.

Two years went by and the Morris's were making it. Hank was working at the paper mill, putting in long hours to pay the bills, while Suzy stayed home with baby Jonah. She was actually starting to get the itch to go find a job and God only knew they needed the money. She was afraid to put little JJ in daycare, for fear that his parents would spend more time at work than with him, but preschool wasn't too far away and he probably wouldn't remember much of this time in his life anyway.

The day she decided to start applying for jobs, she couldn't wait for Hank to get home. She made him dinner—pork loin and mashed potatoes, just like he liked. She set the table, lit some candles and even put on a little makeup. But six-thirty came and went, and then seven. And then it was eight, and she sat at the kitchen table bouncing her toddler on her knee until he was too tired to laugh or keep his eyes open and she put him to bed.

Hank *had* been going out with the guys after work, she knew. But usually he told her on the days they were planning to be out like this. On those days he would get home around nine with beer on his breath and sleep on his mind. She wished that wasn't the case tonight.

Hank walked through the door of their little house at 9:48 that night. His eyes were puffy and red, and his breath smelled like beer even though his demeanor didn't seem like that of a drunk man. He was incredibly serious, and when Suzy tried to ask him where he'd been, all he could say was that he'd been doing some thinking. The life he was living was not the life he wanted. He'd had dreams, he said. He'd had a life—a future—with hopes of a football scholarship and a college education and a real career. Instead he was just a forgotten has-been whose greatest adventures were behind him. They'd had their fun, he said, but they were never in love. Did either of them honestly think they would just grow old together and everything would just be okay? They were just kids after all, he pointed out. It was like they were running a race they had started from an insurmountable deficit. They were never meant to win.

Suzy's head was swimming, trying to grasp the weight of the situation.

"So what are you saying?" she said.

Nothing.

"Shit, Hank, you better answer me."

"What do you want me to say? You want me to say it out loud? That this isn't what I want? That this is never how I saw things going?"

"Saw things going?! You think this is how I imagined my life?"

"But you have Jonah," he said. "You have a purpose."

"*You* have a purpose. He's your son, Hank."

"I don't—I can't be a father…" The tears welled in his eyes.

"Why can't you?"

"Because I'm not good enough. I can't be…"

"Hank," she said softly, fighting the tears forming in her own eyes. "You listen to me. You can't go around wishing to be someone else, because you have to be who you are. People can change. Life can change. But you wake up every morning and you still have to be you. And no matter how badly you think about yourself, or what you think you should be, or could be, it doesn't change a damn thing about who you were born to be. All it can do is make you into that person, that person you were made to become. And that's where you are, Hank. And maybe it's not in some big football stadium, and maybe we don't have a big house, or fancy cars. But this is who we are... and I need you. JJ needs you. This, right here, right now, this is your adventure. This is where your life is."

"I'm sorry, Sue," he said, and his voice cracked for an instant. "It's not anymore."

The screen door clanging shut was the loudest Grandma Brown could ever remember as she listened from the kitchen. She'd stopped by around eight to drop off a pie and a new blanket she'd knitted for her grandson when she noticed the worry on her daughter's face and stuck around to talk.

An engine revved to life in the driveway, and for the last time, Suzy heard the sound of her husband's truck fading into the night.

As Saturday evening drew closer, I found that I was equally as nervous for the bonfire at Josh Williams's house as I had been for the football game. Elle might have had something to do with it. Yes I loved football, and it felt like my life had been intently focused on that first game for a month now, but the bonfire was something completely different. Somehow it felt just as big and important. I hadn't been to many social gatherings like this one; not one that was organized by people my own age and wouldn't require adult supervision, and not to mention the fact that there were cute girls there.

I've now been to quite a few bonfires in my life, but I remember that one vividly.

Josh's dad ran one of the only, and definitely most successful, real estate businesses in Oak Hill, and therefore the Williams family didn't want for much. Their house was set on the outskirts of town to the east and they had a nice plot of land with the nearest neighbor about a half-mile away. It took a good two minutes to drive down the driveway. Out in the backyard was the fire pit, which had been installed when the pool was expanded the previous summer. The pool sat between the fire pit and the house, and there was a perfectly manicured grassy area that separated the garage from the house and led to the driveway with two immaculate-looking cars and a NBA regulation basketball hoop.

There were ten people there when Thomas's parents dropped us off that night. The split was even between guys and girls, or at least would have been if weren't for Thomas and me. Everyone was gathered in an illuminated orange flickering bundle about forty yards from the edge of the driveway. The sun was setting, and its angle caused the house to cast a long shadow over the fire pit and much of the back yard. Josh's parents were inside watching a movie with his younger sister.

When we walked up, the steady conversation evaporated as if it were a Dixie cup of water someone threw into the flames. Everyone stared, waiting for us to state our business. Or something like that.

"You guys know JJ, right?" Charlie said. A few heads nodded around the circle. "Oh, and this is Thomas."

Hacksaw looked at us as if he'd never seen us before. Josh gave me a subtle head nod.

The others started slowly, and quietly, back into their prior conversations.

"Hey JJ." It was Elle. I half-waved and was about to say, "hey," back when one of the other girls, Kiera Nash, spoke up.

"Oh you're on the football team, right?" she said.

"Yeah," I said. I forced a smile and surveyed the people in the circle, noticing Hacksaw and then seeing him quickly turn away before our eyes could meet.

Everyone was staring at us again.

"Did you make varsity, too?" Kiera asked Thomas.

"Uh, no, not this year," Thomas said. "I'm no overnight sensation like this guy." He gestured his thumb at me.

"You guys can come sit over here," she said, gesturing to the empty patch of blanket next to her.

Once we got settled in, things seemed to be a little more relaxed. Josh started talking about how one of the girls in his class asked him out on the second day of school. I don't know that anyone believed him, but it felt like it shifted the focus to him and allowed us to join the group.

After about an hour of awkward conversations and stories, we were sitting beneath a starry sky. The fire flickered orange light across the scene that surrounded the pit as we all sat and talked and ate hot dogs. Charlie had passed out glass-bottled sodas from a cooler that Josh was sitting on, and Elle and Kiera were putting out the ingredients for s'mores on a cardboard box.

One of the guys there, Dylan Albright, went to his car and got his guitar after the s'mores. He played a few tunes, sitting on the drink cooler, and had the girls all looking starry-eyed.

After the second or third song, I got up to go to the bathroom, which was inside the house. It was quiet and dark in there, but Josh's parents had left a few dim lights on before heading to bed. The house smelled like vanilla.

I went back outside, careful not to let the back screen door slam, and just as I turned to head back toward the fire, which had now turned into a full-length concert, I heard a rattling thud.

It had come from the driveway and sounded like a basketball hitting the rim and bouncing onto concrete.

And apparently, my hearing was pretty good, because that's exactly what it was. Elle had left the bonfire with Kiera and one of the other guys to go shoot some hoops (Josh had told them how to turn on the lights over the basketball court). But as I walked up I noticed Kiera and the boy running toward the far side of the garage, giggling and holding hands. Elle was left alone, watching them go.

"I wonder what *they're* up to?" I said.

"Oh gosh!" She turned around, and nearly dropped the ball. "You scared me. I didn't hear you or anything."

"Sorry," I said. "I wasn't trying to be creepy."

She laughed. "Do you want to shoot with me? It seems I have been ditched."

We started shooting around, and she drove me wild every time she would line up for a shot and get this intense look in her eye. She made about half of the shots she took, and I was smitten. She was adorable.

Unintentionally, somehow everything I shot was going in.

"You're pretty good," she said. "Are you a basketball star too?"

"I don't think so," I said. I shot another one from the grass and it went in.

"Seriously, though," she said laughing. "How are you doing that?"

"I don't know. Maybe you're my good luck charm."

She smiled. And we just stood there grinning at each other for a moment.

"Hey, you guys sneaking off over here?" It was Josh. He was with Thomas. "I'm just kidding, y'all are good," he laughed. He walked in a side door in the garage and a moment later, a soft yellow light was spilling from space in the garage doorframe. Thomas and I made eye contact as Elle took another shot, and he nodded in the direction of Elle with a grin.

Josh emerged with an armful of chopped wood and handed it to Thomas. He went back into the garage and suddenly I heard a whoop of excitement. Josh sprang out of the door with a blue box and thrust it over his head with a shout of victory. The white letters on the package's side read "Bud Light." Josh took off on a jog back to the fire, and left Thomas with the load of wood in his arms.

"There's more in there too," Josh's voice echoed from the fire pit. I could see the glint of the shiny blue cans as he handed them out. Thomas was just about to the fire when he dumped the wood onto the ground.

I looked back at Elle who rolled her eyes and then took the basketball from my arms. She shot, and the ball caromed off the rim and bounced down the driveway. She noticed I didn't move and looked at me.

"What's wrong?"

I didn't say anything, because I wasn't sure what I wanted to happen. I didn't think beer was a good idea, but I was afraid that she would want to join the others, and I certainly didn't want to look stupid in front of her.

"Do you want to..." I gestured over my shoulder toward the distant laughing, top-popping noises near the fire. "I mean..."

"Oh, I think beer's disgusting," she said laughing. I felt a little relieved. "Besides, I'm already having fun." Her eyes seemed to sparkle as she said it, and my chest felt like it suddenly was ten degrees warmer. Thomas came back from the fire and joined Elle and me on the basketball court.

"I hate to cut in," he said. "But I don't want to get into whatever's about to be gotten into over there."

An hour later, and after several more trips to the garage by Josh, the three of us were still playing basketball and laughing. We talked about her older brother; how he was cool but full of himself and couldn't pick good girls to date. And we talked about football, school, movies we liked, and music. It was great.

We had just started a game of PIG and were talking about our favorite holidays (hers was Christmas) when she stopped short.

"Oh gosh," she said with her hand over her mouth and nose. "I think my nose is bleeding."

"Are you okay?" I asked. "Did I pass you the ball too hard?"

"No," she laughed, the sound muffled by her hand. "I just get them sometimes. But this is bad timing. I'm sorry."

"It's okay. Do you need a tissue or something?"

"Yeah, probably," she said.

"I got it," Thomas said. He headed toward the back door of the house.

Elle sat down on the concrete, stayed there for a minute, and then laid flat on her back looking up at the stars. "Sorry, this is embarrassing."

"It's really okay," I said, sitting next to her. She looked over at me, into my eyes, and then put her hand on mine.

"Hey!" we heard coming from the direction of the fire. "What'd you do to her Morris?"

It was Hacksaw. He was walking, unsteadily, toward us with a beer can in his hand.

Charlie was jogging to catch up to him.

"Did ya hit her too, asshole?" he yelled, and said something incoherent about a hospital that ended with a colorful flourish.

"Marcus c'mon," Charlie said. She caught up to him. But he shrugged her off like it was football practice and continued toward us. He drank what was left of the beer, crushed the can in his fist, and threw it.

"We're all right," I said. "It's cool, man. Relax."

"No bro," Hacksaw said. He was within a few steps of me now. "I saw you break that dude's arm. You got anger issues or some shit?"

He reached and grabbed the basketball from me.

"You like to hurt people?" he asked.

Charlie was tending to Elle now and drew his attention.

"What happened? Are you okay?"

"I'm fine," Elle said.

"I'll go get you a tissue or something," Charlie said. Elle slowly got to her feet, using one arm, still holding her nose with the other.

"Thomas is supposed to be getting them," Elle said.

"C'mon let's go find something," Charlie said, taking Elle's free arm. She and Charlie started walking toward the house. I started to follow behind them.

"No!" Hacksaw yelled. "We're not done."

"Yes we are," Charlie said. "Elle's bleeding over here. It's gonna get all over her shirt."

Hacksaw insisted we all stay outside, but I didn't want the girls around him like this. Heck, I didn't want to be around a drunk, angry guy that goes by the name Hacksaw. So I sent the girls inside, assured them I would be fine and walked back over to Hacksaw.

"What do you think, you're the king around here now?" Hacksaw said. He stepped toward me. "I want my shot."

"What?"

"You know, bro," he said. He leaned in toward me and I could smell the beer on his breath mixed with the smell of smoke from the fire. "I know about you. I know you're a..." He belched.

I stood looking at him, wondering where he was going with all of this.

"They told me you suck. An' I seen you at practice. You suck." There was a little bit of drool in the corner of his mouth, and his eyes were looking at me like he was trying to hold them open as wide as he could. "You don't even know where to go. You're not a football player. You just got lucky."

"I don't know what you want Hacksaw," I said.

"I want my shot, bro." He threw the ball down on the concrete. "That's supposed to be me." He pointed at me.

Now I knew where he was going.

He circled around me. My back was to the basketball hoop.

"So it's my turn now," he said. He shoved me hard. I fell back, grasping at the pole of the hoop to stop my fall, but I missed and hit the ground like a chair had been pulled out from under me just as I was about to sit on it. I was instantly angry. I wanted to hit Hacksaw more than anything, and he stood looking at me, waiting for me to try. I grabbed the pole to pull myself up and was going to launch myself at him when there was suddenly a shadow covering Hacksaw's face and shoulders.

We both looked up to see the basketball hoop come crashing down onto the concrete. I looked down to where I'd felt the metal beam.

Where my hand had touched it there was a jagged, wrinkly mash of metal. The pole and hoop laid severed, several feet away. I turned to see Hacksaw wide-eyed. He put his hand to his head and then looked at me.

"Shit, bro."

The ride home from the bonfire was pretty quiet.

Hacksaw hadn't said much else to me after our scuffle, and

Thomas's parents got there to pick us up shortly thereafter.

When Charlie, Elle, and Thomas had come back outside and questioned the bent basketball hoop, I just said that Hacksaw had tried to dunk on it. He didn't deny it, and no one seemed to ask any further questions. I told Josh the same thing. He was mad, but bought it. Between the beer, the hoop and God knows what else, I imagine his parents had a few things to say the next day, although he never mentioned anything about it, and I never asked.

Thomas's mom asked us about the night, and was specifically interested in the girls that were there.

But even though Mrs. Winters asked Thomas several interestingly probing questions about Charlie, my mind was busy racing to make sense of what had happened in my (almost) fight. Yes, I had been mad, maybe a little embarrassed or something, but I hadn't intended to break anything, and I certainly didn't feel like I had exerted enough energy to do so. It felt like nothing—as if it were made out of cardboard or something. What if I had done something like that to Hacksaw?

Then it dawned on me. Maybe I had. But it wasn't Hacksaw. It was number 5 from the Carrasco game. That had been a similar feeling. And the lockers. And the hit—

I had done it to Hacksaw after all! I remember asking myself what was wrong with me. Was this something I could control? What was it? What was I?

It was the first time I thought the word: *freak.*

Time was moving the same as it always did, but the weeks that followed the bonfire felt like they raced by at a supersonic speed.

By that point, I was used to the breakneck pace of life as a high schooler. My mom dropped me off (or I walked if she had to work) at school by 7:15 in the morning. I would sit in classes until lunch at 11:45, and then go back to class until 1:50 when I went to my seventh period football lifting class. When the day's final bell rang at 2:35 in the afternoon, I'd head out to the practice field for another two hours before heading home to eat dinner and work on the homework or studying I'd need to have done for the next day. And that didn't include the days I would go and hang out at Thomas's house or go get a burger with some of the football guys. The days surged by like a freight train through the countryside.

I came home from football practice one evening, and my mom told me she felt like she didn't even know me anymore. Between her work schedule at the hospital and my schedule as a full-time teenager we were hardly ever at the house at the same time. She insisted that we sit at our little kitchen table and have dinner together at least once a week, but even those times felt hurried and hard to fit in.

In a matter of weeks, my life felt like it had completely turned upside down in the best way. I was a well-known kid in high school, friendly with most everyone except maybe Hacksaw, I had a spot on the varsity football team even though I still wasn't playing much, I had a date to the homecoming dance (Elle hinted to me—via Charlie saying "I think Elle wants you to ask her to homecoming,"—that she wanted me to ask her, several days after the bonfire), and I was even enjoying school and getting good grades.

Things were good.

My only issue was the nagging thoughts about the incident with the basketball hoop. I was paranoid thinking about what might have happened if something like that occurred at the wrong time, or around a bunch of people. I still didn't know if I could even do it again. Really, I was afraid that being found out would somehow undo all the good stuff that had happened to me in the previous month.

At the same time, I was desperate to talk about it with someone. I still didn't even know what I was dealing with, but I thought maybe talking about it might help. Like when you start to have weird symptoms and you're wondering if you might have cancer or something, and then you tell someone and they say they've had the same thing and that it's just a fart.

I wanted someone to know, and to be able to tell me if this thing I had, or did, or was, was good or bad.

"What do you mean?" I remember Thomas saying when I slept over at his house one night. Maybe it was because my mind was racing, or maybe it was the uncomfortable futon sofa bed I was lying on in his room, but I couldn't sleep and finally worked up the courage to confide in him.

"I don't know, it just happened."

"So you're saying you just sawed their basketball pole in half… without even trying?"

"Yeah, I guess so. It was weird because, now that I think about it, I can remember feeling it… give."

"Give?"

"Yeah, just like… give."

"So maybe the metal was weak, or something?"

"No dude. It wasn't."

There was silence.

"Really, it was a lot like the hit on Hacksaw," I said.

Thomas sat up in his bed across the room from me and turned on the light.

"That... that was...?"

"It wasn't exactly the same. But it didn't hurt or anything."

"Dude... That's—this is crazy!" Thomas shook his head and laughed. I was relieved. "Can you do it all the time?"

"I don't think so," I said. "It only happens once in a while."

"Dude, we gotta try it." Thomas jumped out of bed and ran out the door. Several seconds later, his head popped back into the doorway. "You comin'?"

We went down to Thomas's basement, where his dad had built them a pretty nice gym with a bench press, some dumbbells, a rower, various weight machines, a squat rack, and Thomas's drum set. Thomas's parents weren't as rich as Josh's, but let's just say they weren't poor.

Thomas put every weight he could find on the bar resting on the rack above the bench. It must have been upward of 600 pounds.

I lay down on the bench and gripped the bar. I could feel the cold weight pressing into my palms. Thomas sat down at the drum set and picked up the drumsticks. He fidgeted with them nervously, but never took his eyes off me.

"Do you need a spot, or something?" he asked. We both laughed.

I collected myself, grit my teeth, and pushed with all my might.

Nothing.

It felt like I might as well have been trying to lift the whole house.

I stopped and felt the veins in my neck relax.

Thomas still looked at me expectantly.

"Well," he said.

"What?"

"Go ahead."

"I already did."

"Oh. I thought maybe that was a warm up or something."

"Sorry man."

"It's all right." I could tell he was a little disappointed. I started to sit up on the bench.

"Oh wait," I said.

I lay back down and tried to think of something that might make me angry. I thought of Hacksaw with his arm around Elle. I could feel my heart start to pound. Actually though, I meant to picture Elle, but the image was of Charlie. But it didn't matter. I pushed again, this time with a grunt.

Still nothing.

"I don't think it's going to happen tonight," I said. I got up from the bench.

"It's all right," Thomas said. He set the drumsticks down on the snare drum with a rattling clank, and then walked over and settled onto the bench. Lying back he muttered, "We can't all be as manly as me." He took ahold of the bar and smiled. I instantly walked over to the spotter's place.

"Go for it man," I said.

"Nah, I'm just kidding. I don't want to get a hernia." We laughed. I turned back toward the stairs when I heard Thomas scream. "Help!"

I whipped around and saw his body contort, as if it were bracing for the impact of the weight. I had the bar in my hands before I could understand what was happening.

Thomas sat up immediately and turned around. Then his eyes went wide and he broke into a wild smile.

"OH MY GOD!" He literally jumped and pointed at me the way someone might if you told them to act surprised. But Thomas wasn't acting.

I looked down and saw that I was holding the bar off the weight rack in almost a curl position with both arms. The bar was nearly touching my chest. As I realized what I was doing, I felt my pounding heart thunder in my ears, and I let out a few deep breaths. Then the weight started to get heavy again and I set it down.

Thomas ran over as the metal clanked, and hugged me from the side.

"OH MY GOD DUDE!" he yelled. "I think I'm going to cry or something."

A voice boomed from the top of the stairs. "Are you guys all right?"

We both stopped.

"Yeah Dad," Thomas said, trying to fight back some laughter.

"All right, then shut up and go to bed."

I told Thomas I didn't want anyone else to know about the weights or any of the other stuff I'd told him. He did well keeping his mouth shut, but I could tell there were times it was a tough ask. We sometimes talked about it when we were alone, but even then we had little to say. Thomas would ask if anything else had happened, or if I felt any different, and I would say "no." After a few weeks of asking me about it at nearly every opportunity he started to ease back, and for that I was thankful. I never regretted telling him, but every time he asked me excitedly, and I had nothing new to report, I felt like I was letting him down.

By the time homecoming weekend rolled around that fall, we hardly spoke of it at all.

The football game on that Friday went a lot like the first game of the year and all the others in between; just without me breaking any bones.

I recall looking up into the stands at one point and seeing Thomas at the front of the student section with some of the other JV guys. We made eye contact and he made a motion as if he were curling dumbbells with both hands and laughed as he did it. I laughed and rolled my eyes, looking away, and spotted Hank sitting about halfway up the grandstands. It was the first game I can remember ever seeing him in the crowd at any of my games. He wasn't sitting with my mom. He was wearing a dirty Carhartt jacket with his hands shoved in the pockets and didn't appear to be interacting with anyone near him.

After the game he came and found me. It was a bit awkward

because I always met my mom after we all left the locker room, and she was there as he walked up and tried to make conversation. I was excited he had come, but nervous to see him. I knew the conversation would be brief, and didn't know what I would say. I talked to him infrequently enough that I knew that he knew very little about my life. And while I could guess that he was still working at the plant and spending too much time at the bar (based on the comments my mom made), I didn't actually know much about his day-to-day life either.

He quickly greeted my mom, and then proceeded to ask about my playing time. When I told him I had gotten to play more in a few games earlier in the year, he changed the subject and started asking me about the dance. I told him about Elle, and he asked if she was pretty. I told him she was, and he made some quick remark along the lines of "Be careful, Morris men know how to pick 'em." My mom wasn't amused and said it was time to go. And that's what we did.

Asking Elle to homecoming had been rather anticlimactic compared to what I had expected. I'm not sure what I thought it would be like, but I figured it would be more than just me saying, "Hey, so do you actually want to go to homecoming with me?" in between classes, and her saying "Yeah!" back.

But the dance was fun. I had never been to anything like that, and so the whole corsage-boutonniere, picking her up, seeing her all dolled up in her light pink dress, getting to go out to dinner with our friends (which actually turned out to be a bunch of her friends from the popular table at lunch), taking photos together, the smell of hairspray, perfume, and cologne—it was all a good time. The actual dancing was strange because the songs were a mix of rap, country, and romantic ballads. I'd never been much of a dancer, but Elle had taken ballet and hip-hop dance classes when she was younger and led me through the uncertain waters of the dance floor. By the end of the night I had sweated through my shirt, my light pink coordinating tie hung in a sloppy knot around my neck, and I was having a ball. Mostly, that was due to the fact that an attractive, popular girl was having fun with me. I saw a couple of the other guys and girls stealing glances at us as we danced, or rather as Elle danced and I flailed, in the middle of our dimly lit school cafeteria.

The plan was to just go home when the dance ended, but Elle was always invited to the biggest party and so we ended up at someone's house that was crowded with other sweaty well-dressed people. I really don't remember whose house it was, but I do remember being pulled out the back door by my date. The house had a pool in the backyard, but even though it was much too cold for swimming, the underwater lights were on, giving the patio area a soft blue tint with the glowing water at its center. We stood next to each other, side-by-side. I reached out and held her hand in my own. Elle smiled and then looked up, and so did I. The night sky over Oak Hill always seemed to have a lot of stars, but that one was wonderfully brilliant. As I stared, I could even make out traces of what looked like unmoving smoke far in the distance. I had learned in some science class that I was looking at the edge of the galaxy.

It was incredible.

Just as I let out a sigh of contentment, I felt Elle's hand shift and her other hand, soft and cold, gently came to rest on the side of my neck. Slowly I looked down and met her sparkling eyes staring up at me. She pulled me close, closed her eyes and pressed her lips to mine. They were cold and wet. I felt her body draw in and press against me. I felt my heart beat faster, and a tingle raced down my back. Elle Vance was kissing me.

It was incredible.

10

When I was in high school, my mom worked constantly, or at least it felt like it. Susan Morris, or Suzy Brown depending on who she was talking to, was a dedicated parent, committed to raising her son not to be a victim of another single-parent home. She wanted me to have a future, so she tried to set an example. She worked late, picked up shifts, and even considered taking some night classes to try to further her career. I admired her.

I knew she loved me. That much was clear from her actions. She attended every game, every middle school band recital (which were probably quite painful), every parent-teacher conference, watched cartoons with me, took me to the movies whenever there was anything worth seeing, encouraged my insatiable love of ice cream, and even taught me to throw a baseball in our front yard. When I was younger, she would take me out on "dates," periodically—first dinner and then the mall. It was my job to open doors for her, place the orders at the restaurants (fast food or sit-down), hold her purse while she went to the dressing rooms in the back of all the women's clothing stores, and tell her my "honest-to-God opinion," on the clothes she tried on. She called this exercise "husband training." Really, whatever chore she wanted me to do could be husband training. Sometimes she would make me wash the dishes, or vacuum the house, or do the laundry, or iron her clothes, or clean the bathroom—pretty much anything. But I accepted the tasks, mostly to humor her, and somewhat because I did plan on being a husband someday and thought I might as well get a leg up on the competition.

When I introduced my mom to my first girlfriend, Elle, her eyes lit up and I wondered if the reason might be because all of her hard work in training me to be a decent guy was about be put to the test, if only minimally at first. They talked about me, and about school, and cheerleading, and me again. They were getting along great.

Later when Elle's brother came and picked her up, my mom cornered me in the kitchen.

"She's pretty cute," she said.

"Yeah, I think so." There was a little break as my mom pulled a grapefruit from the refrigerator and a sharp knife from the drawer.

"When did you two become… an item?" she asked as she began to slice up the fruit on a plate.

"Last Thursday," I said. "We talked a few times after the dance. She told me she liked me. Like, *liked* me. Can you believe that?"

Mom laughed. "Sure I can. You're a cute boy. And you're on the football team."

I laughed in a weak attempt at modesty.

"She convinced you at the dance, huh?"

"Convinced me?" I could feel the tone shift in our conversation.

"Yeah, I saw she was wearing your jersey at the last game."

"Yeah, well we're dating now," I said.

"Okay, well I would just be careful if I were you," she said, as she arranged the pieces of neatly speared grapefruit in a circle around the plate. "Elle seems a little fast-paced. I just don't want to see you two end up…" She trailed off.

"What do you mean?"

"You kiss her yet?" She picked up the knife and rinsed it in the sink.

"Well, umm…" I brushed the back of my head with my hand.

"Okay, and who kissed who?"

I stopped, put my hand down and grinned at her. She turned off the water, pointed the knife at me and smiled back.

"Fast-paced."

11

Elle and I spent the better part of the first few weeks we dated making out.

When we weren't at school, and I wasn't at football practices, chances were good that we were on her parent's couch, or in the back row of the movie theater, smooching. We didn't spend a ton of time at my mom's house because of her suspicions of Elle, and due to the fact that my mom was gone a lot of the time and asked us not to be there alone. I made sure we honored that request. The Vances didn't seem to mind much—including Elle's brother. He never said anything much about it during football.

Elle and I did our best to be civil in public, and almost never even kissed at school, except for maybe a peck on the cheek between classes every now and then. I loved it. Elle was great. She looked at me in a way that made me feel like I was important, like I meant something. I had never experienced that, at least not from anyone other than my mom and Grandma Brown. When she was around any of our friends (that's what I got to call them now), whether or not I was there, she would brag about me. She called me a "great" athlete, an awesome boyfriend, charming, hilarious, smokin' hot, and even told the girls I was a good kisser (a compliment I was especially proud of).

Thomas was happy for me at first. He would say things like, "Dude how much are you paying her to go out with you?" and "How does a guy like you get a girl like that?" Once when he and I were alone in the locker room before football, he asked if I had shown her any of my "tricks." I hadn't. Also that sounded weird. Sometimes he would just shake his head and grin at me when he'd see us together, which was a lot. But eventually he got tired of me saying "no" every time he asked me to hang out with him, and he started to call me out for it every chance he got. Elle always said he was welcome to come hang out with us, but he responded by saying he didn't want be a "third wheel," and he wasn't sure how three people could kiss all at once anyway.

I remember that I started sleeping less around that time. It wasn't that I was having trouble sleeping, I just didn't feel tired very often. I would stay up late, watching *Sportscenter*, or reruns of whatever sitcom was on, and then I would wake up at four thirty or five in the morning and feel completely awake, although I always woke up with a few aches and pains in my arms, legs, and shoulders. I had never been much of a morning person, and a lot of the time I would be frustrated when I awoke almost two hours before my alarm was set to go off. But I felt fine.

At the same time, I was beginning to eat more than I ever had. But football season was in full swing, and between class, practice, lifting weights in the mornings, plus all of my extracurricular activities with Elle, I didn't think much of it.

That was until the night Elle's mom was out of town, and her dad decided to take us to Pizza Hut.

Elle's dad, Mike, was the Oak Hill police chief. He had formerly worked in the Detroit Police Department before the Vances relocated to Oak Hill to be closer to their extended family. His stories were always incredible, teetering on the edge of being unbelievable. I thought he was really cool, albeit a little intimidating when he'd walk through the front door in his uniform. The police cruiser was sometimes parked in their driveway, and at first it took me off guard. But the more I got to know Mike, and saw that he was just a guy, the more at ease I was.

Mike had already finished his work day, and was back in plain clothes by the time we went to Pizza Hut that night. We started off ordering a beer for Mike (since he wasn't in uniform) and two large pizzas with plans to take the leftovers home for Elle's brother who had opted to go hang out with his own friends instead of coming with us. The pizza disappeared faster than we all expected, and Mike said something like, "Well I guess we're getting to live a little while mom's gone, huh?" And then, "You think we need another one, JJ?" I told him if he bought it, I would eat "a few slices," and so he did. He ate a slice, and grunted as he tossed the crust onto his plate. Elle ate a few bites off of one piece, and I held up my end of the bargain… and then some. I polished off the last few bites of the last piece of pizza on the table, and I can honestly say I was still a little hungry. I loved to eat anyway, and as a teenage boy I guess it was expected, if not condoned. But this was breaking new ground for me.

I remember Mike sitting back in his chair, watching me chew the last bit of crust in amusement. He pushed his baseball hat back on his head, reached over and grabbed his empty beer glass and lifted it toward our waitress across the restaurant. She came over and began to pull the check from her apron.

"Hold on, Darlene," Mike said, as he tilted his empty glass. "I'll take another, and bring this young man whatever kind of pizza he wants."

Elle watched all of this with a look of stunned horror.

"Dad!" she said.

"It's all right, honey, he's earned it." He said this with a chuckle.

She looked at me. "You can't possibly still be hungry." It wasn't a question. Her dad looked a little wary of her, and glanced over at me.

"Actually…" I said.

"No, this is ridiculous," Elle said with a laugh. Darlene shifted her weight on her feet and looked at us in amusement.

"If the guy's hungry, let him eat," Mike chimed in. "Boy's gotta grow."

Elle looked at her dad, and then rolled her eyes, smiling and shaking her head.

I was unsure if she was actually getting mad or just in disbelief, but I knew one thing for sure.

"I'll have a large pineapple and ham," I said.

Elle groaned and took the keys off the table, muttering something about "paying attention," as she headed to her dad's truck.

Mike and I sat in silence as she left. Darlene returned with the beer and set it on the table before heading back toward the kitchen.

"Was that a fight?" I asked.

"Eh, not sure," Mike said taking a swig from the frothy brown drink. He sighed, and set the glass down. "I've seen worse."

Putting down somewhere in the ballpark of three pizzas by myself was both satisfying and concerning. On the one hand, I was rather impressed with myself. On the other, I was a little worried. I knew pretty quickly that the pizza hat trick was less of an outlier and closer to my day-to-day appetite, or rather meal-to-meal.

It became a regular occurrence for me to eat a "snack" when I got home from school, after football practice. I would be ravenously hungry by the time I walked in the door, and so typically that was the first thing I tended to.

Half a dozen frozen waffles, a box of cereal, five or six eggs, a few strips of bacon, a bag of chips, a loaf of bread, half a jar of peanut butter or jelly, or both, whatever leftovers were in the fridge, and a banana (for potassium)—I could manage all of that in an afternoon, and did so more times than I'd care to admit. But I tried to control myself, at least a little. My mom only went to the grocery store once a week.

A few times when she asked where the food had gone, I tried to cover it up by saying that Thomas or some of the other football guys had been over. She would always just shake her head and say something about "teenage boys."

But she did notice the way I was scavenging for food on an hourly basis, and so we started eating a lot at Jade House because of their buffet. My mom always ordered a Diet Coke, ate a plate of kung-pao chicken and fried rice, and then asked for a to-go box to take some home. Meanwhile, I ate an average of four or five plates of food, a bowl of hot and sour soup, and several helpings of whatever kind of sugary dough they presented as dessert before loading up my own take-home box. I swear, we nearly ate them out of business.

The problem was, that I knew it couldn't continue—not at that pace. We couldn't afford it. I knew my mom made decent money, but I had seen her paying our bills and overheard her asking for extra shifts at the hospital. Hank wasn't very consistent about sending money, but my mom never said much about it to anyone who could do anything to enforce his legal requirements as a father seeing as though they'd never actually divorced.

Because she wasn't a big fan of Jade House, I ate dinner at Elle's house fairly often, though I caught her mom gawking at me, on more than one occasion, as I chomped through yet another peanut butter and jelly sandwich.

Through this sudden spike in food consumption, my appearance never changed. I was still lean and hardened from all the football. I'm told that food is one of the great unappreciated joys of youth. It does always seem ironic to me that life is such that people can afford to eat whatever they want at the same time that they can't afford to eat whatever they want, but then when they can finally afford to eat whatever they want, they can't afford to, figuratively speaking.

Anyway, my experience was, and has always been, a little bit different.

The last football game of my junior year came in early November.

The *Oak Hill Press* reported that the Acorns had been mathematically eliminated from the playoffs and that Briggs's job was in jeopardy, although everyone was aware of those facts several weeks prior. The Golson Raiders were looking to end the season by bolstering their resume and solidifying their position atop the conference with another road win. For them, this was a tune-up game as they headed into the postseason.

Briggs was a nervous wreck. His profanity-filled instruction at practice that week was punctuated with a colorful pregame speech that would have left us smoldering in our seats if we hadn't been sure we were going to lose.

It was hard to believe the season was coming to an end. Honestly, I was somewhat glad. Not playing much for an entire season of any sport, on any team, but especially if your team is bad, isn't loads of fun.

To his credit, Hacksaw was the one bright spot on an otherwise abysmal Acorns football team. I heard rumors he was already getting looked at by a few colleges. I wouldn't have paid much attention to any of that except I had seen a few letters stuffed in his gym locker and heard he and Briggs talking seriously from time to time. I was immediately envious. I was confident the next year would bring more opportunities, and that I might even be able to become a better, contributing player by then, especially if I continued getting stronger. I thought about how that could be useful on a football field.

I remember being insatiably hungry before that game. I devoured a PB&J in the locker room before the game, even though a few of the guys gave me a hard time and told me I was going to throw it up running out of the tunnel.

I didn't.

Austin Marks went down with a knee injury near the end of the first quarter and I saw Briggs throw his clipboard as they carted Marks off the field. I jogged in to take his place. We were losing 10-0. A linebacker and the other safety were yelling out assignments in the huddle. It was third down, and I heard them say "tight hawk I," and "cover two," consecutively. Everyone clapped and started running to their positions on the field. I lined up several yards back from the linebacker in front of me. Golson had been running the ball for the majority of the game to that point, mostly due to the ease with which they were able to do it. I saw their quarterback turn and yell something, then turn back and hike the ball. I shuffled my feet back, and saw a receiver crossing over the middle of the field. The quarterback was hunched down with his back to the play, and the running back was sprinting in front of me off to the right. Our defense was chasing him. But he didn't have the ball.

Instead, the quarterback jogged out to the opposite side of the field and wound up to fire the football clutched in his right hand. It was then I noticed the receiver that had crept behind me. I turned to look and saw him, arms flailing as he ran, and no Acorn uniforms within fifteen yards. Too late, the players on our bench screamed "Pass!" and I heard Briggs above the rest, not saying "pass." I took a final glance back to see the quarterback watching his ball fly through the air, and then I turned, dug my cleats into the grass and sprinted as hard as I could with my head down.

I looked up a few steps later as I saw the receiver's feet come into my view. The roar of the crowd was deafening. And the ball was there in front of me just overhead, floating down into the welcoming, gloved hands of the Golson wide out. But in an instant, I realized I could catch it. I swiped with my left hand and cradled the ball in my palm. I glanced to the eyes of the intended receiver, now wide with surprise, and his body began to adjust to me instead of the ball. A moment later, we were crashing to the ground. There was an audible, collective gasp from the crowd, until I thrust the ball over my head, and then the cheers came descending onto the field in a wave that sent a shiver down my back. I couldn't help but grin beneath my helmet as the ref signaled it an interception and change of possession. I trotted back to the sideline with an escort of shoulder pad slapping and leaping, ecstatic Acorn players. A couple guys hugged me and I caught words like "ridiculous," and a guy singing the riff from *Sportscenter.* Briggs pushed his way through the crowd to me and grabbed my facemask. He pulled my head toward him, almost glaring into my eyes. But then his stare softened and he broke into an exuberant laugh without a word.

In the third quarter I intercepted another pass, though not in quite the same dramatic fashion as the first. That one resulted from more of a wobbly pass, but I found it downright effortless to shrug off the attempted tackle after I had the ball, and practically jogged the fifty-three yards down the sideline to score the first touchdown of my life. The score tied the game at 10-10. They didn't even attempt to throw the ball the rest of the game.

Midway through the fourth quarter, Briggs put me in the game as the kick returner after Golson hit a field goal to make it 13-10. "Let's see what ya got, kid!" he screamed as he slapped my butt when I ran by.

I caught the kickoff and looked up, unsure of exactly where to go. At first I tried to follow my teammates who were blocking trying to clear a path, but once I started running, I maneuvered with ease through the sluggish and oncoming Golson players. I weaved between a few just to draw them all in toward the middle of the field before quickly changing my course and heading up the sideline. I felt like I never broke into my full sprint and coasted across the goal line to give Oak Hill a rarity: a lead in a football game.

It was too easy.

I didn't get a chance to touch the ball again for the rest of that game, but we won 24-13 and Briggs gave me the game ball in the locker room after the game. He leaned in close and whispered, "You saved the day," as he handed it to me while the rest of the team shouted their approval around us.

14

Everyone was gushing over my two touchdowns in the last football game of the year. Briggs highlighted my big plays in our last film session of the year in the week that followed, Hank called again to tell me how proud he was of me, Elle introduced me as her "football-star boyfriend" to her grandma, and Thomas came to school on Monday wearing a white T-shirt with a blown-up photo of my face on the front and asked me to sign it. Even the *Oak Hill Press* got in on the action, headlining Saturday's front page with, "Acorns' Disappointing Season Ends With Budding Talent."

It was almost embarrassing.

Almost.

It felt like everything was going my way. Football had ended well and propelled me to mini-celebrity status, even if it was only for a week or so. My grades came back with all As and one A-minus in English, after I had aced all my midterms. Elle seemed happy. Thanksgiving was wonderful. I actually got to eat two Thanksgiving dinners. One with Elle's family and one with my mom and Grandma Brown. I felt like things were going very well, and better than I ever could have hoped before starting high school.

The only problem was the pain.

I thought perhaps the adrenaline of playing football had caused me not to notice some bumps and bruises I had suffered. But when two weeks had gone by since the end of the season, it felt like it was getting worse. I started to wonder if maybe something else was going on.

The pain regularly woke me up in the middle of the night. Aches in my shoulders, deep shooting pains in my arms and thighs, soreness around my knees, my chest—everything hurt in some capacity.

But the worst was the headaches.

Occasionally, I woke up with my head throbbing so bad I couldn't see straight. Someone told me once that if you ever think you're going to throw up, you should eat frozen grapes; it's supposed to make things taste a little less nasty. I ate a lot of frozen grapes. And, compounding the headache-induced trips to the bathroom was the fact that I was now even hungrier than ever before.

I told my mom early on how I was feeling. At first she chalked it up to me being run down, banged up from football, and with it being winter in Michigan, she said, it was cold and everyone was more susceptible to getting a cold or the flu. But after things didn't change, she thought I might have some sort of infection or contracted mono ("You do smooch Elle, a lot," she pondered more than once), or even maybe something more severe. She checked my temperature, blood pressure, shined a flashlight in my eyes, nose, mouth, and ears. There was nothing out of the ordinary.

I continued to try to go to school for the next two weeks with a hefty bag of pain killers, but there were several days I just couldn't do it. My mom would get a call from the school office asking to come pick me up. A few times, not wanting to make her leave work again, I just walked home. We lived about three-quarters of a mile from the high school, which never felt like a bad walk until I had to throw up in some old lady's bushes and take a break every hundred or so yards because the world was spinning too fast.

Eventually, I just stopped going to school altogether and spent what I think was about three days without leaving my room other than to use the bathroom and grab an occasional snack (mostly frozen grapes).

It was a mid-December day when, finally, after my mom came home from work and saw me in bed yet again, with no signs of the mystery ailment going away or getting better, she scheduled me to go see one of her doctor friends from work.

"I just don't know what's wrong with him, Jim," she said.

Dr. Jim, with his eerily calm voice and his bushy brown mustache, ran all the same little tests my mom did. But when they came back normal he wasn't ready to give up. He called for X-rays. Nothing.

Next came blood work.

And then a CT scan.

I remember going in for my follow-up appointment, and sitting on the table with the crinkly white paper while Dr. Jim straddled a backward-facing black desk chair with his arms crossed. My mom sat in the one other chair in the room with her purse on her lap.

He took a deep sigh.

"Well JJ," he began. I was sure this was the beginning of the end. I guess in some ways it was. "You're not dying. Everything checks out." He grinned at me, seeing my disbelief.

"Really?" my mom asked.

"The picture of health," Dr. Jim said stroking his mustache.

"What's going on with all of *this* then?" I said, gesturing to myself.

"Well, some kids have pretty severe growing pains. You're a little old to be having them, but we've ruled out pretty much everything else. I just think you have an exceedingly severe, and in this instance, painful, case."

"Growing pains?" I asked. The disappointment was probably oozing from my tone.

"But what about the headaches?" my mom asked, looking a bit puzzled.

"Well, do migraines run in the family?"

"No, I don't think so," she said.

Dr. Jim shrugged his shoulders playfully. "Stress at school, over-exertion, not sleeping well—heck, some people are just prone to them. It could be any number of things, but we know there aren't any abnormal masses, or nerve damage, concussions—it's none of that. All the tests came back almost perfect."

He scribbled out a prescription for some extra-strength painkillers and sent us on our way.

15

Because of the pain, I didn't see Elle as often as the blistering pace we had previously enjoyed, and so I was surprised to find out that her family was traveling to Colorado on a ski trip over Christmas break the week before they left.

Thomas and his family always went and visited his grandma in Ohio over the holidays, and even though he and I weren't hanging out as much since I'd started dating Elle, I still became very aware that I was going to be left with two weeks off of school without the two people I hung out with the most.

Waking up each morning in the same amount of pain that I had gone to bed with was enough to make me want to pull my hair out. The medicine didn't feel it was doing anything, and I could only watch so much daytime TV.

My mom was planning our usual quiet Christmas with Grandma and Grandpa Brown, but I didn't have much holiday spirit and felt like a burden on my mom. For maybe the first time, I was aware of how much she was doing for me, and knew it was unfair to her. I thought about other families like the Winters and the Vances, and how everyone was together around the holidays. It was times like that when I became all too aware that my mom was working double-duty, and my heart hurt for her, and a little for me too. I wanted to tell her to just go to Grandma Brown's and leave me to sleep the day away, but I knew she wouldn't.

Typically, we went to Oak Hill Bible Church in the middle of downtown on Christmas Eve. We didn't go to church a lot, but I always thought going on Christmas Eve was kind of fun, even though it felt like they preached the same message and sang the same songs every year. Maybe that was why I liked it. It felt familiar. And then on Christmas morning we would get up early, Mom would drink her coffee while we opened our stockings, and she would go out into the kitchen and finish preparing the breakfast she had started working on the night before. I always went out to "help" however I could, but mostly that just turned into me refilling her coffee mug, eating icing from the cinnamon rolls or whatever delicious thing it was she was making, and sitting at the counter while we listened to Christmas music and talked. Her favorites were Nat King Cole's "The Christmas Song," and anyone's rendition of "White Christmas."

Then when she had finished her preparations, and the oven was preheated, she would slide a wonderful-looking glass pan into the oven, quickly shut the door and turn to me with her eyes wide, wiping her hands on a holiday themed dish towel and say, "Are we ready for presents?"

We would head back to the tree and she would systematically dole out my presents, including whatever Hank had dropped off for me, in the order she wanted me to open them as the sweet smells from the oven wafted over us.

After presents, we would eat our breakfast, and then get dressed for the day and go meet Grandma and Grandpa Brown at the movie theater and see whatever was playing. They always paid for our tickets, and said they would let us pick the movie. But we almost always ended up seeing whatever they were interested in. It was great.

I usually loved Christmas.

But for the first time in my life, I wasn't looking forward to it.

It was Christmas Eve when my mom asked me if I would go to the store with her to pick up "a few things" to take to Grandma and Grandpa's the next day. As much as the aches and pains in my body made me not want to go, I obliged.

We had gotten an unusually heavy snowfall leading up to Christmas that year, and the plow trucks were out in full force around Oak Hill in an attempt to make the roads manageable for the holiday.

There was a sparsely-used back road that took you from the north side of town, where the hospital and my mom's house were, to the main drag on the east side where a lot of the restaurants, shops, and our two supermarkets were. Once we hit the back road, I remember my mom saying something about how they hadn't plowed that road since she was a kid. "When you get a car, I wouldn't want you driving back here when it's like this, but we're a little short on time." I'd only driven a car a few times, but even I could tell driving on this road was not the best idea. As we slowly made our way across the winding road that was hidden under a layer of snow packed down by other cars that had driven over it, I felt the tires slip and the sudden loss of traction sent our car drifting toward the ditch on the left side of the little two-way road. My head throbbed as my body jostled when my mom quickly turned the wheel, trying to regain control. The tires caught again and my mom began to steer us back toward our lane.

She pressed the gas pedal with a bit more firmness and went to straighten the wheel, but the car didn't turn with the tires and we were headed toward the ditch on our right. My mom frantically spun the wheel to the left and pressed the brake pedal. We slowed to a halt, just before veering into the ditch that was filled with powdery snow, next to the edge of a frozen corn field.

My mom sighed and pressed the gas, but the tires just spun and flung bits of snow as the engine revved. I asked if I needed to get out and push, but she said no and that she didn't want me to have to do that since I already wasn't feeling good. She did the typical routine—throw it in reverse and then quickly back to drive—a couple of times, trying to rock the car out of its rut. By the fourth round of this maneuver, our tires caught again as my mom nearly floored the gas pedal, but we were still heading toward the left and skidded directly into the opposite ditch, the nose of the car burying itself into the snow bank. The back end of our car hung out into the lane of oncoming traffic.

My mom looked frazzled, staring at her hands still gripping the steering wheel.

"Well..." I didn't really know what to say that wouldn't make things worse.

"Shh," she said. "We aren't completely..." She whipped the car into reverse and pressed the gas. You could hear the tires squealing atop the firmly packed snow and ice. We didn't move.

I glanced at her to see what kind of mood she was in. "Are we stuck?"

"Well..." She opened her door—or tried to. We were sunk deep enough into the drift that a white wall enveloped the space outside her door. "Maybe." She tried backing out again with similar success to the first attempt.

"Do you want me to get out and push?"

"No, I know you don't feel very good. Besides, I'm not sure what good it would do. I don't think you could even get footing in that."

"Well, what should we do then?" I asked.

"I'll try Grandma, but I doubt she'll have her phone on." She reached behind her seat and pulled out her black bag and began digging through it to find her cell phone.

I leaned my head against the window, and decided I would at least give my throbbing eyes a break from looking at the blinding white field sprawling before us. Just as my head met the cold glass a knock on the outside of the window jarred my senses.

It was Mrs. Jacobsen.

She pulled the scarf covering her nose down to her chin. "Are you guys okay?" she said, muted through the window. My window began to open, and I looked and saw my mom holding the button on the panel on the driver's side door.

"Hi, Deb!" my mom said. "We're fine. Just a little icy out here."

Mrs. Jacobsen giggled. "Well Barry's not here, but we can try to help," she said, and turned to beckon to her car for someone to get out.

"Oh you don't have to do that," my mom said.

"It's okay, Nora and I can try."

A younger girl walked up to the car. I recognized her, although I knew I hadn't seen her in quite some time.

"You remember JJ, right Nora?" Mrs. Jacobsen said. Nora smiled as she met my eyes, then looked down to her boots and the snow. "Nora'll be in high school with you and your buddies next year."

"Mom..." Nora said, obviously embarrassed. I was all right with that reaction. I was sure she recognized me from the football field and probably thought of me as a smoldering older man. How modest I was.

I opened my door to get out of the car.

"What are you doing?" my mom asked.

"I'll push," I said.

"But, what about...?"

"I'm fine."

I waded through the icy powder toward the front of the car. The snow came up nearly to my waist, and my chest hurt from breathing in the cold air on top of the rest of the pain radiating through my legs and shoulders. My mom threw me some gloves from her window.

"Oh, hang on a second," Mrs. Jacobsen said. She turned as a car was heading down the road in the right lane we had been on. She began to wave her arms and walk toward the car. It slowed to a stop and I could see Mrs. Jacobsen walking toward the driver's side window to explain what was going on.

"All right, let's hurry," my mom yelled out the window. The car hummed as she shifted into reverse.

I braced my gloved hands on the grill of the car and prepared to push. Some flurries of snow flew toward me, and I saw Nora struggling to make her way to where I was.

"I can handle it," I said.

She continued to make her way over and positioned her hands in a similar fashion to mine on the front of the car. She looked tiny, half-buried in the snow bank.

"You good?" I said. She nodded. A few snowflakes shook loose that had been stuck in her hair. I kind of chuckled out loud, and then signaled to my mom that we were ready.

The tires started spinning and Nora and I both pushed. I felt extremely weak, and the muscles in my shoulders burned while I strained to move the car. It barely budged, as snow spewed out from the tires. After a few moments the vehicle came to rest back in its original place.

"Okay let's try that again," my mom shouted.

The tires began to spin again, sliding over the packed-down snow, and Nora and I heaved. It moved just barely again, and then slid back to the groove it had made. Nora let out a deep sigh through her nose. My entire body ached.

Just then, I heard a frantic scream from Mrs. Jacobsen, who was in the middle of the road flailing her arms, shuffling toward us. But she was looking past us. I turned to see what she was seeing. A large plow truck was making its way down the road in the oncoming lane with its plow on the ground and snow spraying up in front of its windshield and didn't appear to be slowing down.

"Push!" Mom yelled.

I lunged into position, and gripped the car by the bumper. Nora scrambled to regain her footing and had placed her hands on the car.

The truck continued toward us, looking like it would shear off the back end of our car. It was nearly to us.

The tires on my mom's car began to spin again.

I could hear the whirring and scraping from the plow drawing nearer to my left. A warm sensation ran down my back that almost made me shiver. Strength flowed through my shoulders and down my arms. My abdomen and legs felt sturdy and immovable. But before I thought too much about it, I shoved.

My feet slipped from beneath me and I fell hard to frozen ground, but my mom's car went sliding out onto the road and rotated nearly

180 degrees as the tires caught, causing it to come to a halt almost into the opposite ditch, but mostly on the road. The truck slowed, having finally noticed us, and passed noisily by.

"Whew!" my mom said with a grin out the window. "We made it."

I climbed from out of the ditch and made sure Nora emerged as well. She brushed the snow from her pants and I wondered if she, or anyone else, had noticed my heroics, but no one said anything. I figured that was probably for the best. I still felt the tingle in my spine, and the pain in my extremities seemed to have dulled.

We said our thanks to the Jacobsens as they clambered back into their car, and then we followed them to the end of the road. They continued on straight through the stoplight, and my mom waved as we turned right and headed toward the store, just like we planned.

I woke up on Christmas morning feeling better than I had in a long time. I lay in bed for a while before I got up, which wasn't all that uncommon for me. But that particular morning stands out because it was the day the pain went away.

It was like getting hit by a bus, only to wake up the next day with your body feeling as if it never happened.

And it wasn't just that I felt no pain. I felt good.

Really good.

I remember lying there, still under the covers, stretching my limbs and feeling a buzz of energy hovering just below the surface of my skin. There was dull warmth radiating from my chest and sending shivers of vigor down my spine. I felt like I could jump up out of bed and go run a marathon, crush one of Briggs's "holiday" lifting sessions, and wrestle a grizzly bear, all before breakfast.

For the better part of two months I had spent my time feeling lethargic at best, so the liveliness was refreshing. Then I remembered it was Christmas!

I sprang out of bed and started to get dressed. Striding across my room, I began to recognize the energy I was feeling as strength. But this was no ordinary strength. It was a constant version of the inklings I had felt lifting those weights in Thomas's basement, and pulling the lockers off the wall, and the car, and Bull in the Ring…

This is just me being healthy, I thought, *I was sick for so long.* But I couldn't shake the feeling that I was strong—super strong.

There was this old dresser that sat on the carpeted floor in my room next to my bed. I stored some of my clothes in it, along with a bunch of my mom's sweaters and some of her other wintery garments. I remember helping my mom and Grandpa Brown try to move it once. And I remember the strained looks on their faces, veins bulging in necks, and arm muscles pulled taut. It seemed looming and immoveable to me for most of my childhood. As I became a teenager I vowed to never store anything on top of it again after I'd nearly given myself a hernia trying to retrieve some money that had fallen behind it.

I walked to the dresser's side, crouched, and slid my hands under the wooden base. Then I stood. The dresser angled in front of me. It was effortless. I knew this was just a minor feat, but it felt like the start of something big.

I slid one hand across the unfinished wooden underside of the dresser and shuffled my feet to place myself more centered and lifted all four of the dresser's feet from the ground. I felt the top of the dresser bump the ceiling before I could fully extend my legs or straighten my back, and quickly lowered it back to its original place.

All I wanted to do was fling the door open, run down the hall and tell my mom to come outside with me and watch me try to lift the end of our car—maybe even the whole thing!

My hand was on the doorknob when I remembered Hacksaw's stunned face standing under the twisted basketball hoop at Josh's house. The word floated into my thoughts again like a whisper: *freak.*

I thought maybe trying to lift a car in plain daylight wasn't the right way to go about this—especially on Christmas morning. The neighbors were home. Deep down in my soul, I wanted to see what I could really do and show everyone my new tricks. What would Elle think? Thomas had seen a little, but what would he think of this? And all the kids at school?! Was it permanent? And what would my mom think? Had she ever seen anything like a teenager lifting bedroom furniture over his head?

In my mind, I played out the scenario of walking into our living room, seeing my mom sitting on the couch drinking a cup of coffee, likely her second, and reading the newspaper. I imagined walking over to the back of the couch, squatting down, and shoulder-pressing the whole thing above my head—mom included.

She would probably scream and follow that closely with, "Put me down!" Then she would ask me what I was doing. How did I get so strong? She would tell me that it was obvious I was feeling better. She would look at me with her nurse eyes. I hated it when she did that. Anytime I was sick or injured, the work eyes would appear, thoroughly examining every detail of my face to see what they could deduce. But she wouldn't be able to figure this one out. At least, I wouldn't expect her to. Then she would ask me when this started happening? She would say, "Has it happened before?"

And I would stand there, still me—still sixteen-year-old JJ in his boxers—staring back across the room.

What would I say to any of that? Is there something you're supposed to say when you wake up one day stronger than everyone you know?

Here I am world. Marvel at me.

No.

Opening the door, I made up my mind to keep my mouth shut.

Mom wasn't ready.

Neither was I.

17

It was early in the morning of December 26 that I found myself standing on a country road next to a vast, and mostly snow-covered, cornfield. I was eating a Christmas cookie, holding a plastic bin that held just a few crumbs, with a thermos full of piping hot coffee tucked under my right arm. An old, abandoned looking barn stood dark and looming, and maybe leaning, in the middle of the cornfield near the road. Next to the barn sat an ancient tractor half-buried and overgrown with weeds and grass that had long since died. It was trimmed with ice and fluffy, untouched snow. The sun was nowhere to be seen and everything looked dark, shrouded in tones of black and grey, save for the moonlight that shone brilliantly overhead and shed enough light for me to see surprisingly well.

I looked at my grandpa's watch I'd taken from the kitchen counter the night before, and pressed the button on its side that made the face glow.

4:13 a.m.

As a tradition, my mom and I always stayed with Grandma and Grandpa Brown, who happened to live a few miles from the city limits and our small downtown area, for a few days around Christmas. Seeing an opportunity, I finally found a place and time that worked to test out what I had started to discover in my room the day before (not in a weird way).

I had gone to bed a little after midnight, after finishing *Miracle on 34th Street* with my grandma, and then slept for only about three hours. After lying in bed for as long as I could, feeling completely awake and not knowing what else to do, I got up, got dressed, made a pot of coffee to put in my grandpa's old thermos, grabbed a plastic container of Christmas cookies and my winter coat, and headed down the road a short distance to the field with the barn.

I set the plastic cookie box and the thermos down where a mailbox would have made sense near the barn's driveway that was now hiding beneath the snow. I peeled off my winter coat and laid it beside the thermos.

I walked to the side of the barn where the tractor sat and sized it up. Sitting next to it was a heavy looking piece of metal farm equipment. Maybe a plow? I walked to it, conspicuously stretched for a moment, squatted and slid my gloved hands under it. Ice cracked and slid, and rustled snow fell in a powdery shower as the hunk of metal came to rest in my hands at the end of my outstretched arms. I looked up at the object above my head. A chill, not induced by the cold, ran through me.

Quickly, I set the equipment down and looked for my next lift. Of course, I went straight for the tractor. The metal groaned a bit as I lifted it from a position it had been sitting in for an unknown number of years. I stared at its underside as I held it over my head with minimal effort. I couldn't help but grin. I even took a few steps with it. Admittedly it sounds a bit ridiculous, and it probably looked silly, but hey, I was walking around with a flipping tractor over my head.

What's next? I thought.

My blood was starting to warm in my veins and my heart thumped excitedly in my chest. I took off running as fast as I could. I heard the crunch of snow under my feet as I made my way across the corn field, and even felt my shoes slip a bit with each step as the ground shifted beneath them. But in a matter of seconds I was standing near the dark tree line. I looked back to the path I had traversed and could barely make out the small dark shape of the barn several football field lengths away.

Now typically, standing out in the middle of a dark field, next to a bunch of trees, would have been a little creepy for me. There are coyotes in that part of Michigan, not to mention anything else my mind might have imagined to be lurking out in the night.

But I felt no such fear.

In my own estimation, I was invincible.

My blood coursed hotly through my veins.

Strutting into the midst of the trees, I spotted the dark, looming form of a fallen tree trunk, although I was almost on top of it by the time I saw it. One of its thick limbs had apparently snapped in the fall and was laying separate on the ground. It would have been heavy to move—even to drag—but manageable for most men I knew. I wielded it like a baseball bat and swung it against a nearby tree, sending shards of wood spraying in a satisfying crunch. I eyed the dead tree trunk, knowing exactly what I wanted to do. I stooped low and hoisted the tree over my head like a military press. I was never one to scream during a workout, although I saw many of the senior guys do it (especially when there were girls around), but at this moment I belted out a triumphant roar. I threw the tree with all of my strength. A moment later I heard it crash into another tree and pleasingly thud to the ground in pieces. The whole thing was incredible. I couldn't believe what I was doing. Another tree trunk laid just a few dozen yards from me. It was long and thin like a telephone pole, but still much too large for anyone to lift. I couldn't leave just the one behind, plus I was having so much fun! So I picked it up, and then balanced it with my right arm so it stretched in front of me like a spear. I remember wondering how far I could throw it, imagining myself standing on the edge of a football field so I could measure. I took a few leaping strides, and then threw it like a javelin, high and arcing over the dark silhouettes of the treetops. It disappeared into the dark. Stillness and quiet crept in, and I realized how loud I was being. I hoped I hadn't woken anyone up, but I wasn't worried. I heard my throw crash land, booming and echoing from what sounded like another football field away. I shrugged, knowing I had no idea of the distance and also that it didn't matter. No one else could do that.

I examined my hands and arms in the dim moonlight. I looked the same as I had. But I was not. This was something new. Something fortunate. Something life-changing.

And then in an instant, I was charging back toward the barn, leaving a trail of violent, icy footprints, and reaching the tractor within a few breaths.

What else? I thought.

I walked to the edge of the barn and looked straight up. I could barely make out the edge of the roof against the starry backdrop. I took a few steps back, and then lunged forward and leaped with all my might. I soared through the air. I felt a bolt of panic strike my spine as the top of the barn passed through my line of sight, my limbs flailing as I realized I was looking down at its slanted roof. But my trajectory was correct, and as gravity pulled me down I headed toward the snowy roof. My feet braced for the impact, and with a crunch of snow and wood, I hit the surface. But the flat surface dented and gave way, and I found myself dropping. I crashed through a thick wooden beam that splintered, and then hit the dry earthy ground of the barn floor with a thud.

I took in a deep, full breath as I lay flat on my back. There was a little tinkling of wood chips hitting the ground around me. I sat up, assessing my condition. I felt fine. Good, really. Unharmed.

Just then, a creak sounded somewhere above me, and more snow from the roof came crashing down. I brushed myself off and looked up, seeing a beam of moonlight streaming through the newly formed, and even more recently widened, hole in the ceiling twenty or thirty feet overhead.

I shivered.

My breath rose visibly in front of me as I exhaled.

Getting to my feet, I jogged to the door, pushed it open, and went quickly to my coat. I slipped it on and hoped my coffee was still hot.

I leaned down to pick up the thermos, and heard a groan from the barn that made me pause. But then all went still and quiet.

Steam poured from the top of the thermos as I unscrewed the lid, and I poured myself a bit of its contents into the tiny, shiny metal cup that normally acted as a second lid on the body of the thermos.

Another groan emerged from within the barn doors, and I saw the whole structure begin to lean toward the tractor. I felt the rush of adrenaline flooding through my body. The barn never disintegrated to pieces, but instead, folded down on itself like a noisy cardboard box.

The barn sat destroyed, and I felt a twinge of guilt and remorse. I was panicked and a little embarrassed, hoping no one had seen what had just happened. I scanned the area, and listened.

Nothing.

I felt a sense of calm creep over me, and I took in a big, chilled breath. Deeper, I felt a sense of power, and I grinned. No one in the world could do what I just did.

I *was* a freak.

I shivered again.

A cold freak.

18

Realizing you're different from everyone you know is a little shocking.

Embracing it is freeing.

Over the days that followed my new discovery, I deliberated on whether or not to tell anyone else.

Thomas already knew a little, so I thought it wouldn't hurt to let him know the rest of what was going on. Of course I should tell Elle, and probably my mom. Heck, maybe even Hank.

Truthfully, I wanted to tell everyone I knew, but there was something inside urging me to keep it quiet. As a junior in high school, I would never have called myself wise. But that's exactly what the feeling in me was—wisdom disguised as uneasiness. Maybe fear.

I imagined dozens of scenarios where I fought off every bully in the school and then walked around with my chest puffed out and my head held high. Or maybe I'd steal the show at the next pep rally by dunking a basketball from half-court. Or maybe I'd rescue a baby from a burning building and be the hero of Oak Hill. The girls would love me.

But in the end, I felt like showing or telling crowds of people would probably be more trouble than it was worth. Sure I'd get to have some fun performing a few "tricks" for my friends at school, but then what? Word would get out and then I'd have people wanting to know about me—what I was. They'd want to know my intentions. If I could level a barn on accident, then surely I could do far worse on purpose. People would be scared of that. Scared of me. And they'd look at me like I was some kind of… freak. In the bad way, I mean. In the, "Don't talk to me," and "Stay away from my family" kind of way.

And then who knew what might happen after that? What if it got outside of Oak Hill?

Would the police get involved?

Scientists?

Doctors?

The FBI?

I'd seen enough movies to imagine what might happen to someone who was different from literally everyone else on the planet. Did I want that? Did I want to risk it?

This was the conversation I had with myself daily, if not hourly, for nearly the rest of that holiday break.

I also pondered why I was this way.

As far as I knew, I hadn't been bitten by anything radioactive, or fallen into a vat of gene-altering goo. I hadn't found any sort of magical medallion, and my parents and everyone else in our family seemed pretty normal.

I actually asked my mom if there was any chance I had come from another planet. She looked at me as if I had. I tried to play it off like a joke. I even called Hank just to make sure and asked him if anyone from his side of the family was exceptionally athletic. He wasn't much help, saying he didn't think so but wasn't quite sure, and then mostly just talked about his glory days on Henderson Field.

There was nothing. No clues or trail that seemed to lead anywhere that might hint at why I was this way. It was frustrating to say the least, but that didn't stop me from using my newfound physical prowess.

19

I told Thomas in the snowy parking lot of Lou's Donuts (an Oak Hill staple) on the second-to-last day of Christmas break. We were sitting in his dad's silver Buick La Crosse, scarfing down chocolate sprinkle donuts and milk. Thomas had just returned from Indiana the night before and had been eager to put his two-week-old driver's license to good use.

"Wait, jumped *onto* the barn?" he said through a mouthful.

"Yeah."

"From the ground?"

"Yup." I was smiling unintentionally.

The image of sixteen-year-old Thomas hunched forward in the driver's seat clutching a half-eaten donut with one hand and combing through his hair with the other in contemplation, is forever etched into my memory. He was looking out the windshield in fading disbelief, as if viewing my story on a movie screen.

"This is nuts man," he said.

"I know." I couldn't help but laugh a little bit. It felt absurd to be telling someone about lifting tractors and crashing through barn rooftops. This was the kind of thing you only ever saw in comic books. Watching someone else try to comprehend it all was laughable; I couldn't wrap my own head around it. I grabbed another donut from the box on my lap.

We talked through some more of what had happened and began to put the pieces together about the other strange instances we now realized were related to this. The hit. The lockers at school. The basketball hoop. I even thought about the car and snow plow just a few days prior.

"And then there was this tree and if you thought those weights at your house were—"

"Wait, wait. It's *on* all the time now? Like, you could just pick up one of these cars right now?" he said, gesturing to the few other cars nearby in the parking lot.

"Uhh, yeah I guess so."

He gave me an expectant look. Then he flicked his head toward the cars.

"Right now?" I knew this was just Thomas messing around, but I felt a streak of panic creep up inside my chest.

"Yeah, why not?"

"I can't. Not with people around." As if on cue, someone tapped on my window. I turned to see three of the other football guys grinning, and the sun shining over their backs and illuminating the steam pouring from their mouths in the cold. I hadn't even noticed them walk out of Lou's. I rolled down my window.

"Sup Morris?" one said.

"Gentlemen," Thomas replied.

"Winters, go away and send back Summers," another barked. We begrudgingly laughed and bro-nodded back. They all laughed. "Nice one," one of them said as they headed to a snow-covered car a few spaces away.

"So?" Thomas picked up where we'd left off, once the doors of their car had all thudded closed and my window was sealed.

"Dude." I was starting to get a little annoyed, but I had no idea what to say. I know I didn't want to get out and lift a car at a donut shop in the middle of downtown. "They'll think I'm a…a—"

"Badass?"

We both laughed. The thought *was* enticing.

Secretly I wanted that—to be seen as someone impressive, with something to offer the world. To make girls jealous of Elle because *I* was dating her and not them, and to make guys jealous of me because they knew they weren't on my level. To command respect. To be important.

"So it's really real, huh?" Thomas's question came cutting through the warm air from the car's heater, and I felt a prickling on the back of my neck. He was acknowledging the gravity of this thing, and someone else saying it made it feel all the more true and weighty. "I mean, you know I believe you, but… I still keep waiting for you to tell me this is all a joke or something."

"I don't know what it is," I said laughing. "If it's a joke, I don't get it."

"So what are you going to do?"

"What do you mean?"

"I mean, like… are you going to fight crime or something?"

We both laughed after he said it.

"I don't know… Should I?" The laughter died down like a train slowing to a halt and then we were just sitting there in the parking lot looking a little suspicious as we both tried to imagine a crime-fighting version of JJ Morris. Another Lou's patron walked by.

"Well," Thomas started. "Why not?"

"What?"

"Why not? Why not be a… I mean, that's what they all do… in the… comics, right?" Thomas sounded like he was trying to explain where babies come from to a first-grader. "I mean look at Peter Parker or Bruce Wayne."

We both laughed.

"Yeah I guess that's true." I said. "Although, those guys had a reason. They were basically forced into it."

"Yeah…" Thomas said. The quiet crept back in. "You tell Elle, yet?"

"I haven't seen her. She's still in Colorado."

"Oh. Is she going to freak out?"

"No," I said as earnest as I could. "I hope not."

"What about your mom?"

I stared at the glass door at Lou's that had "Go Acorns" written across it in hand-painted red letters and a yellow-frosted donut with red sprinkles painted below the words.

"No, I… I don't know what to say to her. 'Hey, Suzy, your boy is a freak. We're going to need to leave town.'"

"Well," Thomas said after a moment. "Thanks for telling me first." He shifted the car into drive and the engine groaned noisily against the icy winter. "Your secret's safe with me Clark Kent."

Later that day, Thomas and I drove out to the country and I showcased my newfound party tricks while he sat in his car with the heater blasting and watched—nothing short of amazement radiating through his expression. It probably looked like the most unassuming circus act of all time, until, of course, I lifted the car over my head.

He leaned his head out the window and yelled something I won't repeat.

When I set him down, he floored the gas pedal of the Buick. Running next to a car down a wintry country lane was surreal to say the least. Better yet was watching your friend's face as he watched you, not only keep pace, but climb into the open window and slide into the passenger seat of his car moving at sixty miles per hour. I brushed the snow from my shoulders and hair. I was hardly winded. Thomas just shook his head.

"This is going to be a lot of fun."

That night Thomas and I decided I might as well get a head start on my now probable life of comic book adventures.

He told his parents we were going to stay the night at my mom's house. I called and left a message for my mom, saying that I was staying at Thomas's house and that I'd see her at church in the morning.

In reality, we sat in the Buick on a side road of downtown Oak Hill, just after midnight, with a twelve-pack of Mountain Dew and a backpack full of beef jerky, chips, and jellybeans. In our minds, it was a "good old-fashioned stakeout," though admittedly, neither of us really knew what we were staking out, or, in fact, what a real stakeout actually involved.

We had waited until Mr. and Mrs. Winters had gone to bed, confirmed that we did hear Thomas's dad snoring, and then I pushed the Buick out of their driveway and a hundred yards or so down the road before Thomas started the engine, to ensure our stealthy getaway.

I wore sweatpants, a crew neck sweatshirt, boots, and gloves—all black save for a red bandana tied around my neck, mirrored ski goggles, and a blue knit winter hat. I'd found most of it in the Winters' coat closet.

The plan was to find some crime (yes, crime), or at least something shady for me to investigate.

Oak Hill's downtown is by no means a sprawling metropolis. In fact, it would be far better to say it's the opposite—a sparse collection of buildings five stories and under that comprise the six-block stretch referred to as "downtown." By day, it bustles with business at the bank, some small shops your grandma would probably enjoy, two antique stores, a resale shop, a nail salon, Sir Venny's Jewelers, a convenience store, a handful of restaurants including Jade House Buffet, a JCPenney, and, of course, Lou's Donuts.

As I'm sure you've guessed, there's never been a whole lot of nightlife in Oak Hill. The lone bar, Tiny's, was about the only thing that ever drew any sort of a crowd after dinnertime. So it was there that we decided to focus our attention.

Mr. Winters's Buick was parked in a row of cars on the street with a clear view of Tiny's front door.

"All right," I said. "Now what?"

Thomas was tearing open a Slim Jim with his teeth, but managed: "We wait."

"For what?"

"Something to happen."

An hour and a half later, nothing had happened. We'd seen maybe a dozen people go in and out of the bar without so much as spotting one ill-meaning patron in their midst. I kept my eyes trained on the door, and followed the movements of anyone passing by, which weren't many. It wasn't long before I noticed a soft snoring sound coming from the driver's seat next to me, and looked to find Thomas with his head resting against the window and one arm propped underneath it for support, eyes closed, a chummy look on his face.

At that point I'd had enough of the stakeout and decided to go and have a look around. Surely there wasn't any seedy behavior going on in plain sight. We needed to look in the dark underbelly of Oak Hill—the alley that ran from the back of the bar to Jade House.

I gingerly shut the car door after silently slithering from my seat, so as not to wake my sidekick. Once the door was latched I crept across the street toward the alley trying not to crunch too loudly on the thin layer of ice and snow on the road. I thought better of walking right up to the alley's ominous opening. *Rookie mistake,* I thought. I could hear voices coming from within the darkness, and chose to skulk along the edge of the JCPenney next door.

I need to be on the roof. That's always where things happen in the comics.

So, I made sure no one was around to see me, and then, from the sidewalk just a foot or so from the brick wall of the JCPenney, swung my arms back and sprang onto the roof, about twenty feet above the ground. I landed with an unanticipated *THUD,* and immediately flattened myself to avoid being seen.

"What in the hell?" I heard from below. It was a man's voice—low and raspy. "Did you hear that?"

Nothing.

I listened for a moment longer, and then slowly army crawled toward the edge to get a look at the owner of the mysterious voice.

I remembered to pull my ski mask down over my face, and peered over the dropoff.

I saw a man wearing a brown jacket with a stained white half-apron that hung just below the form of his sagging belly beneath a black T-shirt. His stringy hair laid across his forehead, and a puff of smoke came from behind the cigarette that appeared to protrude from a thick black mustache. He pulled the jacket tighter around him, and shivered. He wasn't anyone I had ever seen before.

"It's too damn cold out here anyway." The man took a long drag on his cigarette, tugged it from his mouth and then flicked it toward a heap of garbage next to a dumpster. "I'll be back in an hour with the stuff." He turned, pulled open the grey metal door that had been propped open behind him, and disappeared inside.

Who was he talking to? I wondered. *And what 'stuff' is he talking about?*

Hoping I had just stumbled across a high-stakes drug deal, I greedily leaned my head a bit farther out from the edge of the roof to get a look at the second man. But as my vision swept the ground, past the dumpster and the old silver trash can, and the pile of soggy card-board boxes and the still-glowing ember of the discarded smoke, and the garbage that drifted lazily in the soft breeze, I couldn't see anyone.

Either they're well hidden, or they know—

I heard a cat's meow, and saw a calico cat sitting on top of a black milk crate, staring up at me from fifteen feet below.

I lurched away from the edge of the roof, heart racing.

All of my excitement evaporated in an instant, and I was suddenly very aware of how cold I was, lying on top of a roof in January, in Michigan.

I yawned and decided I was ready to head back to Thomas's house. I pulled myself to my feet, and was just about to hop down to the sidewalk when I noticed the black and white police car parked behind Mr. Winters's Buick. The red and blue lights weren't flashing, but the headlights were on and steam poured from its tailpipe. An officer wielding a heavy-looking flashlight was leaning on the Buick next to Thomas's open driver's door. Thomas sat with his feet on the pavement, turned sideways in the driver's seat, looking up at the policeman, who I recognized as Elle's dad, Mike Vance.

With no believable excuse for napping in a parked car on the side of the road across from a bar at two in the morning, Thomas had simply told Mr. Vance the truth—he was waiting for a friend. Understandably skeptical, Mr. Vance asked Thomas a bunch of questions to try to decipher if he was up to no good. But after several minutes, it became obvious that Thomas hadn't been drinking and didn't appear to be high or anything else he wasn't supposed to be, other than young and out past his curfew. Mr. Vance told him to just go home, and not to give any other officer a reason to think he was a hooligan on his way.

I held my position on the roof and came down only after both cars had pulled away. Thomas and I met back up at his house and discussed the details of how the night had been a complete letdown, and how it had nearly made us out to be the villains when all we were trying to do was be the good guys. After we'd each polished off a bowl of Frosted Flakes, we headed to his room, and I lay down on my usual spot on the futon sofa bed stewing over what had gone wrong.

20

I was still thinking about that strange night as I sat in my first-hour US History class before the bell rang to signal the start of that Monday—the first day back from Christmas break. I looked around at all the other people sitting around me, and coming in from the hallway. *None of you know,* I thought, smirking in my mind.

Then suddenly, the conversation of the room jarred me from my thoughts.

"Has anyone heard from Allie?" It was a girl sitting a few desks over from me turned around in her chair and addressing anyone who was listening.

"What's wrong with Allie?" someone else asked.

"You didn't hear?" the girl said, concerned.

"Oh yeah something with her house, right?" someone said. "A fire or something?"

"No, it wasn't a fire," the girl explained. "The roof caved in. A tree fell on their house."

I felt like I had just dropped a hundred feet on a roller coaster.

"A tree?" another boy chimed in, sounding puzzled. "I don't think they have a lot of trees by their house."

"Well, it didn't just fall out of the sky," the girl said. "They have some out there."

"Yeah, but I don't think there's any close enough to fall on their house," the boy said.

"JJ, your grandparents live out that way. Does Allie's house have trees by it?" the girl asked.

I was trying to comprehend everything I was hearing.

"I don't know," I said. "Is Allie... her family... are they all okay?" My stomach twisted into knots as I spoke.

"She's fine, but her dad had to get taken to the hospital," the girl said, pulling a newspaper from her backpack. She offered it to me. "Her and her mom, and brother had to go stay at her grandma's in Midland for a little while. The house is pretty messed up. They're trying to get it fixed."

Before me sat a three-day-old copy of *Oak Hill Press* with the headline "Mysterious Tree Branch Pummels Country Home," on the front page and a much too close-up shot of the huge limb sticking out from the roof in the midst of scattered shingles and debris.

Beneath the photograph, the article reported on Allie's dad. "Rogers was rushed to Oak Hill Memorial Hospital by EMS first responders with reported injuries to his lower body."

Injuries?

The article went on to say that the other members of the Rogers family were "medically cleared" and sustained minimal wounds, but that the same couldn't be said for the two-story home, of which the damage was significant both to the exterior and interior.

"What remains a mystery is how the large piece of wood came to rest on, or in, rather, the Rogers' home," the writer explained. "Experts speculate that perhaps a strong gust of wind could have moved such an object, but that no such weather has been documented in recent days, and is not typical for winter months in mid-Michigan. A nearby barn also appeared to sustain damage from an unknown cause.

"Surely, this tragedy is not the result of a practical joke gone too far, or some sort of menacing hoax, but any information possibly related to this incident should be reported to the Oak Hill Police Department. Authorities continue to investigate this seemingly unnatural occurrence."

How did I not think about houses nearby?

Why did the log have to hit that house? Why couldn't it have just missed?

I looked around at the faces of all the other students as they continued to talk.

None of you know, I thought.

I have to keep it that way.

Walking through the hallways of OHHS after the dismissal bell, I was still trying to make sense of the whole situation in my mind, when a pair of arms enveloped my waist and a body hit me squarely, and came to rest against my own.

"I missed you," Elle said. "You feeling better, babe?"

"Wha—?" Normally, an interaction such as this with your beautiful girlfriend would put you at ease. But I was afraid to talk for fear I would be tied to the busted-up house out in the country. My mind raced to catch up with my surroundings. "Oh, right. Yeah. *Much* better."

"Good," she said. "Is there something you want to tell me?" Her eyes sparkled as she said it.

"What?" I probably sounded more defensive than I should have.

"Thomas said you had something to tell me."

I cursed him in my mind.

"It's nothing."

"Oh, come on. What is it?" She smiled expectantly, and ran her index finger across my chest.

"Really," I said, grabbing her wrist. "It's not the right time." I didn't know what to say without lying, and I was afraid I wouldn't be able to hide it. So much was different since we'd last seen each other. And in light of the news I had just heard, I regretted telling anyone at all, even if it had only been Thomas.

"What's wrong?"

"Nothing."

"Nothing?!" The fuse had reached its end. She wrenched her hand free from my grip and pulled her books to her chest. Her stare was hard. "I haven't seen you in two weeks, and you're going to act weird and not say anything? What's with you?"

"I don't know." It wasn't a lie.

"Whatever." She turned to go. "Let me know when it's a good time for you." She was shaking her head as she walked away.

I stood alone in the middle of the hallway while a few hundred students hurried past on either side.

I had never felt more alone.

That night, and for many more, I dreamt of flying tree trunks, burning houses, and accusing newspaper headlines.

Elle didn't talk to me for a few weeks after that day in the hallway.

Honestly, I didn't mind it all that much. I didn't really want to talk to anyone. In my own estimation, I had narrowly escaped from the jaws of discovery and prosecution.

My secret remained intact.

By not saying anything to anyone other than Thomas, I was hoping to keep it that way, and maybe, just maybe, the Rogers wouldn't ever find out I was responsible for thousands of dollars' worth of damage to their home, not to mention their uneasiness of always wondering if another tree was suddenly going to slice through their ceiling.

I felt confident that Thomas wouldn't talk, especially after I voiced to him, rather loudly, not to ever talk about it to anyone ever again. He never asked me directly if I had anything to do with the Rogers's thing, but I think he knew I did.

When Elle finally did decide to speak to me again, it was as if nothing had happened. She came up to me one day, wrapped her arms around my neck, kissed me, and said she was sorry and that it was all her fault. Who was I to say anything different? *No, really it was me. I'd had a rough day. I had just found out I destroyed Allie Rogers's house by throwing a tree...* That wasn't going to happen.

Things went back to basically normal, and I did my best to lay low, only indulging in the use of my "fun" skill set when I was alone, and to make sure I still had it.

I remember walking through the school, or seeing some of my friends at the movies, or talking to my mom and grandparents at dinner, thinking *They have no idea who I am.*

To the outside world, my life looked as pedestrian as any other high school kid in the good ol' USA. I was always hanging around school, talking about how I couldn't wait for football season to start back up, dating my girlfriend which was basically just us making out after school and at the movies or anywhere else we were, and holding hands at our lunch table and while we watched Detroit Pistons games on her couch with her dad drinking a beer in the recliner three feet away, with his feet up. I was playing video games with Thomas, and getting in trouble in class for talking to Thomas.

But to anyone who was paying close attention, they would see a kid whose grades had miraculously rocketed to near the top of his class because he didn't have to sleep as much as everyone else. Waking up at three thirty every morning and staying up past midnight every night gave me ample opportunities to study. And it didn't hurt that my memory was significantly improved. I could hear something once and recall it with ease on an exam, or on the football field, or telling Elle some juicy gossip I heard walking down the hall.

If you looked closely you'd see a gangly football player eating Chinese take-out by the truckload and rarely making it more than an hour or two without stopping to eat something else. And you'd see that gangly kid growing into a lean athlete without so much as breaking a sweat in the weight room.

Other guys were grunting their lungs out to hit their maxes and get their name written at the top of lists. I could've done it with one hand, but instead I held back. I went through the motions, spotted for the other guys (even Hacksaw a time or two) and did my best to camouflage into the swirling sea of smells, and sweat, and dirty jokes, and smart alec comments, and know-it-alls, and muscle poses, and the highly sought attention of the opposite sex—the world of teenage boys.

No one suspected a thing.

During the last few weeks of my junior year, I got an idea.

Senior pranks were a regular occurrence with everything from the low-level stuff like spray-painting various renditions of male genitalia on the practice sports fields or getting a group of thirty students stampeding down the halls screaming, to the more intricate tricks like reprogramming the bells to ring twenty minutes earlier than scheduled.

Spectating students were always enamored with the mischief (given they weren't on the wrong end of the joke). The school faculty was less in favor of the senior antics, although I think they secretly found them amusing.

I had done well to not draw attention to myself for the entirety of the spring semester, at least not for the wrong reasons. But deep down, I was itching to use my hidden talents for more than just impressing Thomas and not having to find rides to places around town (so long as it was early in the morning or late at night).

So on the seniors' last day of school (they always got out a few weeks before everyone else) right before our end-of-the-year exams began, a guy named Aaron suddenly yelled out "Oh my god," as he looked toward the window during class, while Ms. Ewing was in the process of reviewing useful vocabulary words like "backpack" in Spanish. Of course we all looked to see what would cause such a reaction, and there, outside the window, was a green pickup truck leaned with its tires resting against the outdoor brick wall of the gymnasium. The truck looked as if someone had attempted to drive it up the wall, had gotten stuck, and abandoned their endeavor.

Principal Cook, Coach Haines, and the janitor were all standing with their backs to us, a few feet from the obscure scene.

I snickered to myself as everyone reacted, instantly making guesses as to how the seniors pulled it off.

Ms. Ewing, her Spanish lesson upstaged, sat down at her desk with a sigh.

Leaving Elle's softball game the night before, I had noticed one lone truck left in the middle of the parking lot in front of the school. It didn't look like it had belonged to anyone who had attended the game, and there didn't appear to be anyone left in the building.

Hoping the truck would still be there, I snuck back to the school at 3 a.m. and sure enough it was. Working quickly, constantly checking over my shoulder, I giddily carried the truck to the back side of the school and leaned it against a wall where I knew it would only be visible to a few classrooms, one of them being Ms. Ewing's second-hour Spanish II class.

The seniors took some major heat for that one, though no one ever denied doing it. They loved the legend that would be passed down from it, and loved it even more when the school had to call a crane crew to come take it down.

That Friday evening there was a party at Josh Williams's house. In name, the party was for seniors as a sort of informal send off. More so, it was an excuse to have a party.

A bunch of the football guys were there with their girlfriends and that included Charlie and Hacksaw. I went with Elle and her brother, but Thomas couldn't go, and so we sat by the pool (away from the basketball hoop), talking with some of the other people, saying how much we would all miss the seniors and how we couldn't believe we would be juniors and seniors the next year.

As the night wore on, as was customary at the Williams' house,

Josh lit a fire in the fire pit. Everyone huddled around it, looking at the stars, laughing together, and reminiscing about the school year. There was a sense of sadness in it. I know it probably sounds dumb and emotional, but it's true. It felt like life was hurtling forward and somehow leaving me behind. I had always dreamt of the days that I would no longer live in Oak Hill. And the seniors, at least some of them, were getting ready to move on with their lives. They were heading out into the world to see what it held for them. Who would they marry? Where would they live? What career would they choose? I wanted to be at that point—to be there, in those shoes, making those choices. I had an entire year of high school left. Was I excited for football season? Of course. Was I looking forward to prom and all the hanging out I was going to do with my friends? Sure. But in that moment, I could almost taste the idea that there was so much more out there. And especially with my new "situation," I felt an immense sense of optimism, a vast expanse of opportunity and imagination welling up inside my chest.

As I contemplated these things, I wandered over to the pool and sat near the edge of the water, staring at nothing in particular as the hum of teenage chatter and silliness padded the background.

I'm not sure how long exactly I sat there before I heard soft footsteps coming toward me on the concrete. I turned, thinking I'd see Elle, glad to have someone to put my arm around and pull close against me.

"Mind if I join you?" It was Charlie.

"Of—of course," I said, taken off guard and fumbling through my words. It was maybe the first time I had ever talked to her without Thomas or anyone else around, and I was suddenly very aware of that. She sat down near me, facing the pool like I was, with a few feet of open cement between us.

"Elle said her brother had to leave, so she had to go with him," she said. "She told me to tell you. She said she'd call you tomorrow."

"Oh," I said. "Thanks."

"Are you guys doing okay?" she asked. "Things seem different between you two lately."

"I don't know," I said. "Maybe."

"Well, what's going on?"

"I don't know. Things are just different."

"Are you guys fighting?"

"Eh... Not really. I don't know... Sort of."

"Any particular reason?"

"I don't know. After Christmas break, things just haven't been the same. We're fine... Yeah, we're fine."

"Well good," she said looking up at the stars. "You guys are really cute together."

"Thanks," I said with a laugh. "Well, what about you and Hacksaw?"

"Oh," she said, sounding like she rolled her eyes. I couldn't quite see her face in the dark. "Yeah, Marcus is good. I just don't ever see him anymore. He's always in the gym, or watching football film... You know what he's like... He really wants to play in college."

"Yeah," I said. "That's good." I was trying my best to be reassuring.

"Yeah, well maybe it is, *for him*," she said. She smiled and adjusted her sitting position. "I think you really drive him crazy."

"Me?"

"Yeah."

"Why?"

"Because you're good," she said. I could feel my cheeks suddenly warm. "He didn't like that you hit him in practice like that, and that your name's been in the paper. I had to pretend I didn't know you very well when I first started dating him." We both laughed.

"Well... Sorry."

"No, it's probably good for him. At least, my dad thinks so." The laughter surged again. And then our eyes met in the dark.

"You know... I miss you, JJ," she said. "You *and* Thomas." She looked away.

"Yeah," I said, trying to figure out what I should say. "Yeah."

"I miss history class with you guys," she said. "Things are just… well, they're just different now. Boys complicate things." She seemed sad.

"Hey," I said, sarcastically. "I resent that." She laughed.

"Yeah, but you know what I mean," she said. "Sometimes, I wish I could go back in time… I don't know. I wish I could go back and make different decisions. I could make things the way I want them… I guess I need to figure out how to get superpowers or something so I can do that."

Superpowers. The word sizzled in my ears.

In the months since Christmas, I had thought it briefly only a couple of times in the back of my mind, like hearing some far away storm rumbling in the distance. Thomas and I had, of course, talked about it, but never at length. It felt like dangerous territory to enter.

This was the first time it felt real; the first time I let myself be fully connected to the word. It was the first time I had come to grips with the idea—standing up in front of it and looking it in its eyes: *I* had superpowers.

"Yeah, superpowers," I said with a slight smile. "I guess that would help."

22

The school year finished, the seniors graduated, and while everyone else in school got three months of summer vacation, those of us on the football team only got about three weeks, much to the disappointment of our girlfriends. But even those days weren't entirely our own.

Briggs held open lifting and conditioning for anybody looking to get what he called "a good jump on the season." It was much less optional than it sounded.

Guys who had been on JV the previous year had to be at almost every session if they had any hope of securing a varsity spot. So Thomas and I went for a few hours every day of "summer," really just to make Briggs aware that we had been there. Thomas was anxious about his playing time heading into our senior year. I thought he would be the easy choice, as the previous year's starting quarterback had graduated a few months before. Nick Montgomery was the other senior quarterback on the roster. He thought of himself as the incumbent starter after getting to play in a few of the games the year before but no one, including Briggs, if he were being honest with himself, thought Montgomery was anything special on the field. The other barrier, at least in Thomas's mind, was this incoming junior kid named Aiden. The way people talked about him, you might have gotten the idea he was the second coming of Joe Montana. Tall for his age, he could throw the ball well and run a little bit.

I was far less concerned with my own football prospects. I didn't know of anyone else in the world, let alone in Oak Hill, who could lift more, jump higher, or run faster than me.

The first time I bench-pressed after Christmas was during workouts in the spring semester. We were in the middle of our football lifting class and I had one of the other defensive backs, named Aaron, rack the weight the strongest guys on the team were attempting. He looked a bit surprised, but dutifully clanked the weights into position. I was unsure of how heavy it would feel in my hands. When I lifted the loaded bar from its resting position on the rack it felt like someone had replaced it with a broom handle. I held it for a second, then quickly re-racked it and said something about biting off a little more than I could chew.

Since that time, I had resigned myself to *acting* like lifting weights was hard. I would always lift enough to be impressive, easily outperforming the other guys my size, but never encroaching on the territory of the linemen or the other strong types on the team. It wasn't like I needed to lift anyway. I was still getting stronger, and my muscles were wiry and hard. I looked like an elite athlete in great shape. But knowing that people might get suspicious if I just magically got stronger without trying, I would grunt while I lifted, and splash water on my face before and after to make it appear as though I was giving it everything I had. Truthfully, the most difficult part of the whole thing was trying to encourage Thomas, or whomever I was lifting with, and pretending I was interested.

I was eager for the season to begin.

I started to think seriously about my future the summer before my senior year of high school. I'd heard plenty about the importance of ACT scores and scholarships from the time I'd stepped foot in Oak Hill High School, but I had never given much thought to what I wanted to do when I grew up.

As a kid, I always dreamt of playing professional football for the San Francisco 49ers. Once I reached my freshman year of high school, it felt like the NFL was probably a long shot. Through my sophomore and junior years, any time I was confronted with the idea of a career I struggled to come up with anything. I didn't really want to pursue what I'd heard OHHS graduating seniors talk about, like engineering, or education, or economics. That all sounded boring. Working in the medical field seemed noble, and I admired my mom for doing it, but I never felt like that was for me either. I really enjoyed my English and writing classes, but wasn't sure how to turn that into a job. At that point, all I knew was that I was desperate to do anything other than end up like Hank, working in a job he hated, constantly living in the shadow of his former glory.

With my new "abilities," I was confident that my best days were ahead of me, even though it felt like they were a million miles away.

Most importantly, this new development in my life made my dreams of professional football seem realistic again.

I had witnessed the envelopes marked with official university logos getting shoved into the lockers of a few upperclassmen on the football team. Rumors were that Hacksaw, as an incoming junior, had already received a few from smaller schools.

Finally, it felt like there was a clear path in front of me. My "abilities" were going to open a lot of doors for me, I knew that much. Maybe football would get me into a good school on a full ride. But maybe football wasn't even necessary. Maybe I would become some sort of celebrity and be in movies and go on late night TV talk shows, and bypass college altogether. At times, it felt like the world was at my fingertips. But most days, my mind was less on the distant future, and more on the present one.

Every time I would start to think about college, or football, or even video games, I would remember Charlie sitting there talking to me by the pool. I felt embarrassed—almost ashamed—as I lingered on my memories of her and Thomas and I laughing in history class, and sneaking around the church kitchen looking for donuts, and going to church summer camps together. My mind recounted the scene of seeing her at the beginning of the school year—how much of a surprise it had been, and how different she looked. And I thought of her and Hacksaw walking together in the hallways at school. And I thought of Elle.

Elle, my girlfriend.

Boys complicate things. That's what Charlie had told me.

I was starting to believe girls were the problem.

Right before the school year ended, Coach Haines pulled me out of lifting class one day and took me into Briggs's office.

Coach Haines said they were considering the idea of trying me out on offense either as a receiver or tailback and wanted me to get some extra work in over the summer.

"We've noticed the work you've been putting in," Briggs said. "And we like what we see."

All the things I wanted to say swirled in my mind, but I didn't have time to get them out before Briggs continued.

"Now, I've got an old friend who's helping with a football camp for offensive players, and I already talked to him. He said he can get you in and get the fee waived."

"Oh," I said. "When is it?"

"July," Briggs said.

"Well, I'll have to check with my mom. I don't know if we have plans."

"You tell your momma to cancel your plans. Football is your plan now. This is going to be good for you, and great exposure for our program. Tell me you won't let us down."

On the second day of camp, I met a guy named Derrick. He was tall and lanky, but solidly built and was raising eyebrows with his ability to catch nearly every ball thrown his way during the pass-catching drills. He stood in front of me in the line to catch passes on fade routes, as a middle-aged man with a whistle on an orange lanyard barked information about form and technique in front of us. Derrick wore a sweat-soaked grey T-shirt, shorts, tall black socks, bright red Nike cleats and a gold chain around his neck. I saw a gleam of light shimmer off his ear as he turned to look over his competition in line behind him, and I noticed a fat gaudy fake diamond earring in each lobe. The whistle screeched and Derrick dashed through his route around an orange cone and caught a football with one hand.

"Y'all wish you had hands like me," he said to a few of his buddies as he trotted back to the line and lazily tossed the ball to the thrower.

"Save it, Marshall," the whistle bearer grunted with the silver accessory tucked between his teeth. He pulled the whistle from his mouth and said to the coach next to him, "If that kid weren't so damn talented, somebody would beat the teeth out of him." The coaches chuckled together and then the whistle blew again.

I matched the one-handed grab on my turn—the ball floating through the air like a beach ball, and me feeling like I could've stopped to tie my shoe and still caught it. Derrick took notice. When I did it again, the next time through the line, he was nodding his head when I came back to the line behind him.

"Okay, okay," he said. "Somebody came to play." I smiled, trying not to let on that catching footballs with one hand was about as easy for me as ripping off a fart. But Derrick was one of the best (if not *the* best of the unaided) athletes at the camp, and had, as I became aware later, interest from dozens of prestigious programs around the country. We spent nearly the rest of the afternoon locked in a duel of sorts; him always performing some sort of drill in a way no one else on the field was capable of, and then watching to see if I could match him. A couple of times I would bobble the ball, or make an intentional misstep, or let myself be tackled, just so I did not appear perfect, but every time I looked at Derrick after my turn was over I'd see him with a grin on his face, or shaking his head. As the day wore on and the sun began to set, the grin showed itself less and less, and was replaced with a look of tired resolve.

By the time we sat down to dinner in the cafeteria, I'd learned that Derrick Marshall, even though he was only going into his junior year, was a superstar three-sport athlete at his high school in Muskegon. His friends and family called him Boogie which was short for "Boogieman," and all of them were pretty sure he'd be a shoe-in for the NFL Hall of Fame.

"Where did you sign, Morris?" he said as he shoveled a piece of grilled chicken into his mouth.

"Sign?"

"Yeah. Like, where are you playing college ball?"

"So far, I'm not."

"What?" He nearly spit out his mouthful. "Who'd you get offers from?"

"Offers? I don't think I have any yet."

"You don't have any? Not even one? Aren't you a senior?"

"Yeah," I said. I was thinking about how up until Christmas I hadn't had any athletic ability a college program would have wanted. "I haven't heard from anyone, *yet.*" Boogie sat back and took a contemplative mouthful from the dinner roll in his hand.

"Well, you will. Nobody can hang with me on the field. But you came pretty damn close." I was flattered, even though I knew his praise didn't even begin to account for what I was truly capable of. *If you only knew...* "I just got a letter from OSU, man," he said.

"Ohio State? Like, the Buckeyes?"

"Yeah, man. *The* Ohio State."

"That's awesome! Is that where you're going to go, then?"

"I don't know, and if I did I couldn't tell you," Boogie said laughing. "But, for real, my momma doesn't want me to go that far. She wants me to stay here and play for Western, or Grand Valley or something."

"Grand Valley State?" I said, surprised.

"'Cause it's right down the road," he explained.

"So it's Grand Valley then?"

"Hell no, man. I don't want to go to no school that ain't on TV. I'd go to Michigan or MSU or Notre Dame. Any of them will work."

"Will work?"

"Yeah, to get me what I want."

"Which is...?"

"The NFL, man..." he said. "I was made for the League. And I can't wait to get there. The fun's already started, I can't even imagine what'll happen when I've got the money, and a big house, and a Lambo." He laughed, delighted in himself. "You know what I'm saying Morris?"

"Yeah," I said with a laugh. "That sounds like a dream."

"Not a dream," he said, turning serious. "The future, and I'm on my way."

I nodded along.

"You gonna be too," he said. "You could have anything—anyone—you want. Girls love a football star. I mean you ain't as pretty as me, but still, you got skills. They'll see. You're set, bro, I'm telling you."

I could feel my pulse quickening at the vivid picture in my imagination. But then a thought interrupted the fantasy.

"But, what if it doesn't work out? What are you gonna do?"

"Man, I don't think like that, and neither should you," he said, irritated. "I'm gonna make it; I'm gonna make sure of that. You just gotta bury 'em, Morris. You gotta bury 'em."

He held up his plastic cup of ice and Gatorade.

"To the future."

Derrick and I didn't stay in touch. Honestly, I haven't seen him since. But I thought a lot about what he told me at that football camp.

Boogie had confidence. He seemed to know exactly what he wanted in life. He oozed charisma and a clear understanding of the journey in front of him. And he appeared to measure up to the task. He would reach the status of celebrity and along with it he'd gain power, adoration, respect, and appeal. What he wanted *was* appealing, wasn't it? His quest was to pillage and plunder the world. I mean who wouldn't want to just be able to do exactly the things he wanted to do all the time without worrying about anything else? There seemed to be a black hole at the center of what he said, pulling me toward his way of thinking even in the days and weeks and months after we talked. It sounded like a hotel room service life—whatever I want, they bring. The thought had dawned on me: *Everything he talked about could be mine.*

And yet, as I thought about the possibilities and even started to look at some of the universities I might want to attend that would help get me these things, there was a nagging feeling somewhere deep within my mind.

A small voice was talking back to Boogie and to me, and although it couldn't be heard by anyone else, it asked the question: *Is it all enough?*

Thomas and I, and a few of the other guys were walking out of the locker room toward the practice field to run wind sprints on one of the last days of summer conditioning when we saw Hacksaw and Charlie across the parking lot, standing apart, looking serious. Hacksaw stood with his hands on his hips, a white sweat towel slung around his hulking neck, and a dark v-shaped splotch on the back of his grey shirt indicating the urgency of their meeting. Suddenly, he waved his arms in a look of exasperation. We all slowed to stop and watch as Charlie crossed her arms and looked down at her feet. Hacksaw gestured with his hands between them like he was arguing a foul in a basketball game. Charlie said something, and then Hacksaw pulled the towel onto the top of his head with one hand and turned to look away from her. Charlie walked away, wiping the corners of her eyes with her fingertips and climbed into her car. The engine roared to life a second later, and the car was veering off across the parking lot toward the road. Hacksaw still hadn't noticed us standing there, and so we all resumed our walking and hurried toward the field.

Later, on a water break, an orange Gatorade cooler clattered into the wooden side of the weathered equipment shack that stood next to the practice field. Everyone turned to look and see what caused the noise just in time to see Hacksaw heaving a second plastic water jug at the wall. That one erupted with a flourish, sloshing liquid several feet into the air before tipping on its side and emptying the remainder of its contents onto the ground.

Of course, Briggs and a few of the assistants scrambled over and immediately asked us what the hell was going on, and told us that was no way to act no matter what some girl did to you.

As we were running our punishment sprints for Hacksaw's outburst, I looked to see Hacksaw slogging through the runs expressionless and staring at the grass in front of him the whole time, while others shot him contemptuous looks and made under-their-breath comments about it all that were still loud enough for everyone to hear.

I can't say I really minded the whole scene. The running wasn't bothering me at all, and Charlie apparently wasn't with Hacksaw anymore. That was fine by me. I grinned as I thought about it. But that was too far. Coach called us over to him after we'd done about six sprints telling the guys that we weren't taking this seriously, that I obviously wasn't working hard enough (because I'd hardly started sweating), and that if I could still smile during sprints we needed to do more.

Pulling me along by my shoulder, Briggs walked to the front of the group of doubled-over teenagers with their hands on their hips or knees, gasping for air, and said, "Here's the deal boys. We *all* work hard. We can't win games if even one of you has his head up his ass. Today one of us isn't doing all that he can do to help this team. He's jacking around, and he's more concerned with his own daydreams than football. So here's what's going to happen, we're going to run. And we're going to keep running until the only thing this guy can think about is running. And the only way I'll know we're there—the only way I'll know he's committed—is when I see your ol' pal JJ puking his guts out."

Briggs licked his lips and held his silver whistle to his mouth as the guys grumbled in exasperation. He blew a quick shrill squeal and we were off and running. I was trying to figure out exactly how it was going to work since I hadn't exerted myself enough to even feel lightheaded by doing things like racing cars on foot and lifting farm equipment. But, then I began to think about Derrick's words—making people respect me and wish they were me and all that. So I just kept running; whistle after whistle, step after step, altering my stride so as to not look superhumanly fast, which felt about like trying to jog next to your grandpa pushing a walker. But still, I led the pack each time down the field. Guy after guy dropped out, hunching over the trashcans, or lying flat on their backs. Coach stared at me as I ran and paced back and forth. There was still a small group of us running. I saw Thomas pull off to the side and drop his hands to his knees, his chest heaving. The whistle blew again, and now there were far less footsteps pounding the grass. One guy fell down and just lay there, as if he'd fallen straight onto the most comfortable bed in the world. Before long it was just Hacksaw and me. Wheezing next to me, Hacksaw pumped his arms and legs, straining to stay even with me. I had to give him credit, he was a freak athlete in his own right—just not the same kind as me. We reached the finish line side-by-side, Briggs blew another whistle, and we turned to run again. Hacksaw gave me a hard elbow in the ribs and grunted as he ran ahead of me. *You gotta bury him, Morris,* I thought. I kicked out hard and passed him in three strides. He gasped in a surprised exhaustion, and then growled as he tried to regain the lead. But it was to no avail. As I, and then he, crossed the end line, Hacksaw collapsed to one knee on the grass.

With little hesitation, Briggs blew the whistle again, and I took off running. I knew this couldn't go on forever, but I wasn't about to let him try to embarrass me—not when I could do something about it.

Six, seven, eight sprints later, Briggs was clicking his stopwatch realizing I wasn't slowing from sprint to sprint. The other guys were just watching, not even mad, but purely amused. On the ninth solo sprint, I decided that any more might get me more attention than I was after. I slowed to a walk and approached Briggs who was looking me in the eyes through his dark sunglasses. I played up some heavy breathing, and put my arms over my head, feigning tiredness.

"We done here? Because I can go all day," I said. It came out in a harsher tone than I intended, but it made my point.

He looked at me and then spit at the ground.

"Yup," he said, and clenched his jaw. "You all get out of here! Practice is over."

Our eyes stayed locked for a long moment as the guys sluggishly pulled themselves up and began to make their way toward the locker room. Finally, I broke our stare and walked past him. He grabbed my arm.

"Morris," he said. "Save this shit for game days."

I walked toward the locker room with a smile on my face, finding myself wishing that Charlie had stuck around a little while longer.

Conditioning gave way to football practices, and the season was back into gear as we neared the end of summer break. I had already been informed that I would assume the role of one of the two starting safeties since I already had game experience and Austin Marks had graduated.

Coach also mentioned that he wanted to try me out at running back (for the record, we never spoke of the incident on the practice field; in his own twisted way, having a punk kid like me pull some crap like that on him might have been just the kind of thing that earned his respect).

When it came time for the quarterbacks to square off against a live defense, I was on the field playing safety.

Knowing that Thomas was being considered among three players for the starting varsity quarterback job, I knew the season would be a lot of fun with him and me getting to play and contribute to the team together.

So anytime he was on the field, I pretended to be completely confounded by the plays he made. I would position myself perfectly to make a play on the ball, or cover a receiver, and then just move ever so slightly to allow the play. A lot of Thomas's throws were okay, a few were actually really good, and several were nothing short of atrocious. But with my help, he looked NFL ready. With the assistance of my superhuman abilities, I never made what I was doing obvious enough for even the most trained eye to detect. They thought Thomas was legitimately good. I couldn't help him with everything, but Thomas was a smart kid and he knew the playbook far better than Aiden Marks, and I made sure that Nick Montgomery never completed a pass against a live defense when I was on the field.

Thomas was named the starting quarterback by the third week

of July. He didn't say anything to me following the announcement that led me to believe he knew that I was helping him. He might have been under the impression he had legitimately gotten the best of me all those times.

I was fine to let him think that.

Honestly, as much as I loathed the practices that summer, I was ecstatic about the football season. My life, at least in the realm of sports, felt like a video game. I was capable of anything I wanted to be capable of on the football field, and I knew that meant that other areas of my life were bound to get more fun as well.

26

One night, during that summer, Thomas, Elle and I got invited to a party at Charlie's house. Mrs. Haines welcomed us in through the front door of their country home that sat nestled atop a hill at the end of a winding dirt driveway a few miles from the heart of Oak Hill.

It looked impressive, at least in comparison to the small house my mom and I lived in. Thomas and Elle both had nice homes—or nicer than mine—but the Haines' was by far the best of the bunch. The main level was beautiful with a kitchen with enough open space to house a small wedding's dance floor and a family room that felt like a mix between a hunting lodge and a small movie theater.

The strange thing about being there was seeing Coach Haines wearing oven mitts, pulling snacks out of the oven for us. He seemed much more laid back, and somehow more human in his own home than he ever did on the field.

Charlie quickly ushered everyone who wasn't her family down the stairs where we discovered that the basement was finished in a sort of makeshift pub—complete with a pool table, shuffleboard, and a bar that was really just a classy looking wooden countertop that separated the rest of the basement from a stainless-steel refrigerator with some sodas and bottled waters in it.

But the basement was nothing compared to the backyard.

As I stepped out onto the back porch, I saw a wide expanse of grass covering the small rises and valleys straight back to the piney tree line that bordered the back of their property some 100 yards from the house. In the far left corner of the yard there stood a large tree with a tire swing hanging from one of its branches and several boards nailed to the trunk at varying angles forming a ladder. There was a small fire pit there in the ground, with a few large rocks arranged around it as chairs. Off to the west, to the right when you walked out of their back door, the yard sprawled to a fence line that separated the edge of their yard from the steep plunge into rolling fields as far as your eyes could see, with an outcropping of trees here and there, and a red barn somewhere in the middle distance of the scene to make it a near-perfect country backdrop.

The sun was almost done setting when we stepped outside that night, making it feel like we had just unknowingly become part of a painting.

Charlie told us they'd bought the land with a "family discount" from her grandparents, Coach Haines's mom and dad. They lived just down the road, and Coach Haines had promised Charlie's mom, who worked as pharmaceutical sales rep but had a secret love for interior design and a keen eye, that he would build her a space to decorate.

It sounded like a fairy tale.

As many of those nights we spent around fires went, we ended up roasting marshmallows and eating s'mores (somehow always forgetting to have napkins on hand), staring at the stars, and talking about much deeper things than everyone intended. On this night, Charlie, Thomas, Elle, and I were joined by Aaron Phillips (the kid from Spanish), Rachel Beverly, who was a friend of Charlie's from church that also went to OHHS, Stacy Everett, a mutual friend of Thomas, Charlie, Rachel, and I, and Aaron's friend Mikey Lang. Thomas and I knew Mikey a little bit, but he and Aaron were almost always together and played in a band together outside of school. They were musician types with wild hair and an eccentric sense of fashion.

The most striking thing about that gathering was that outside of Thomas and me, there weren't any football guys there; and other than Elle, no cheerleaders. After I made varsity we spent most of our time around other people related to the football world during our junior year, even though they weren't really our natural friends. It was a fresh experience to be away from the jocks.

The later it got, the louder Mikey got as he told more stories and cursed at nearly every opportunity. He had a knack for being in places where there were cute girls, especially cute girls without boyfriends, and none of the ladies there that night, outside of Elle of course, were dating anyone.

After jumping over the fire on a dare, and then again without his shirt on, Mikey dared Stacy to join him. She giggled and shook her head, but Mikey persisted until she was leaping alongside him, shrieking as they cleared the flames. Then Mikey turned his attention to the rest of us.

"Truth or dare?" he asked Rachel.

"Really?" she said.

"C'mon, c'mon. Truth or dare? And really, you know you have to pick dare, right?"

"Okay," she said, after a moment. She was obviously not amused. "But I'm not taking my clothes off."

"Fine, fine," Mikey said, raising his hands like someone was pointing a gun at his chest. "Kiss Thomas." He gestured next to her, where Thomas sat, eyes suddenly wide.

Even in the orange tones of the firelight you could see her blush.

"On the lips," Aaron added, and Mikey nodded in agreement.

"This is so stupid," Rachel said, rolling her eyes.

"Hey," Thomas said in his most offended tone. "I'm right here."

She leaned close to him. "Shut up," she said, and pecked him on the lips.

Mikey and Aaron roared with excitement, and hungrily looked around the circle for their next victim.

"Elle," Mikey said.

"Who put you in charge of this game?" she said, looking mildly amused.

"Are you playing or not?"

She rolled her head toward me, and smirked. I smiled, and gestured toward Mikey.

"Fine," she said.

"All right," Mikey said with eagerness dripping from his voice. He was looking around, searching for just the right amount of torture. "Moon a car."

"What?!" she said. And several of the other girls chimed in as well.

"Oh, come on," he said. "I'll do it with you." He walked over and extended his hand toward her.

Elle hesitated, swallowed hard, and then grabbed his hand and stood.

For at least ten minutes they stood waiting by the side of the road, the rest of us looking on from a "safe" distance.

Finally a car drove by, Elle bent and as modestly as was possible, revealed her derrière from beneath her jeans. Mikey bent over and dropped his pants to his ankles, and shook his hips back and forth, and yelled. Elle joined in his scream. The car's lights silhouetted the two figures and then sent out a quick burst of three honks as it whizzed by. We all laughed.

Elle buttoned her pants back into their proper place and smiled sheepishly as she walked toward me and the rest of the giggling bunch, who greeted her with pats on the back and lots of raucous laughs.

"All right," Mikey said, once we were all grouped up, crunching through the dry grass as we headed back toward the fire. "It's your turn Charlie. Take off your—"

"Whoa, whoa. Slow down there, big guy," she said. Everybody chuckled, including Mikey.

"All right," he said. His brain seemed to whir as he thought. Then inspiration leapt into his eyes. "This is a truth… What happened with you and Hacksaw?"

We all walked without speaking for what seemed like a half-hour, with no sound but the crunching beneath our feet. Elle grabbed my hand.

"I..." Charlie started. "We just... I don't know."

"Well, c'mon," Mikey said. "It's just a game."

"I know," she said.

"Leave her alone," Elle said. "If she doesn't want to talk about it, then don't make her."

We were approaching the fire, and everyone sat once more.

"Yeah," Charlie said. "Can't I just kiss someone and be done with it?"

"Fine," Mikey said, standing with his hands on his hips in front of the fire. He still wasn't wearing a shirt. He looked at Aaron, and I saw one of Charlie's eyebrows raise.

Mikey turned back to face her and grinned.

"You have to kiss JJ." He shot a glance at Elle. She didn't appear to move.

"Mikey," Rachel began. He held his up his hand to stop her.

"We're all friends here right? It doesn't mean anything. I'm sure Elle's fine with it."

Everyone turned to look at Elle, who looked suddenly aware that she might ruin Mikey's (and apparently everyone else's) fun. She shrugged her shoulders, as if to say, "What the heck?"

I looked hard into Elle's eyes, trying to decipher any hidden messages she might be trying to send my way. She stared straight back, but didn't change her expression.

The awkward moment hung over us like a dense fog, and my heart seemed to be beating harder than it had in a while.

Finally Charlie moved, lightly touched one hand to my shoulder and kissed me. I felt the warmth of her lips pressing against mine, and the brush of her soft cheek on my face. The smell of her perfume was intoxicating with its bright, flowery notes rushing toward me in our closeness. And there was a gathering excitement welling up in my chest. And then in an instant, it was over. But the feeling of her lips lingered on my own. Knowing it was someone different than Elle felt so strange.

"There," Charlie said, her eyes still looking at me. "Nothing to it."

In the days that followed that night at Charlie's house, I found out that Mikey had a big crush on Elle, which completely makes sense in retrospect.

Elle never really said anything specific about any of it. I expected her to ask me something, or make some comment about how dumb Mikey was, but she never did. In fact, the entire car ride home that night, neither Thomas, who was driving, or Elle even so much as acknowledged that any of it had happened.

The first week of school coincided with the first football game of the season. We had a pep rally that Friday where Briggs gave a rousing speech, although no one seemed to be as into it as he was. But he ended with "Are you ready for some football?!" and that did the job. By the time we started filing out of the red and yellow adorned gymnasium the crowd was sufficiently roused. Everyone was excited to be back, and even the looming prospect of homework and standardized tests didn't seem to dampen anyone's spirits. There was a buzz surrounding the new semester that seemed to brim with energy and promise.

That night we played Carrasco. I had always loved it when the year started with our rivalry game, but it made the anticipation even greater, knowing that I would be playing in it.

I could hardly wait.

I was dressed and ready, sporting my new number-three red jersey, before all of the guys had hardly even made it into the locker room. I was like a ticking bomb, a ravenous lion on the prowl, a rock star preparing to take the stage, and those analogies cycled through my mind as I stood, fidgeting with my helmet near the doorway, while Briggs talked about new beginnings and hustle and never giving up and other such coaching clichés.

The crowd seemed even louder than I remembered it when we ran onto the field with the band playing our fight song, *Hail Oak Hill!*

From the skies in swelling echoes,
Come the cheers that tell the tale,
Of your vic'tries and your heroes,
Hail Oak Hill! We sing all hail!

The sound of the crowd shouting those words sent a shiver down my back, beneath my shoulder pads.

It's my turn now, I thought.

And it was.

On the very first play of the game, the Carrasco quarterback dropped back to throw from the Pioneer thirty-eight-yard line, and as he did, it was as if every person on the field started moving in slow motion. He wound up and heaved, and I could see his eyes looking down the field to his intended receiver. The ball seemed to hang in the air forever, and I felt like I probably could've grabbed it at any point (especially if I really wanted to wow the crowd), but I was persistent to keep things under wraps, and so I waited until the ball was fairly close to the receiver before closing in and snatching it away. I turned to see a stream of Pioneer players clumsily plodding toward me. I effortlessly pushed the first away, and then jogged (and I did have to jog to make it look realistic) around the rest to get to the sideline, and then coasted into the end zone.

Briggs met me on the field before I reached our sideline. He smacked my helmet and then grabbed my facemask and pulled my face as close to his as was possible, staring at me with a wild grin.

"This is going to be a hell of a year," he said, almost whispering through his gritted teeth.

When Carrasco got the ball back, I had to stop myself from doing the exact same thing again. Every pass the quarterback threw was easily within my ability to intercept, but I knew that for one thing, some of the passes would take a superhuman effort to catch because they were being thrown to the opposite side of the field from where I stood, and for another thing, no one intercepts every pass the other team throws.

So I resigned myself to let the Pioneer offense make some plays. These were things I had already thought about during my hours of unneeded practice, but the game and the crowd and the lights all made it hard to not be as awesome as I wanted to. I made a few tackles on Carrasco's second drive, being careful not to hit anyone too hard.

After the Pioneers scored on a field goal to make it 7-3 (I had to hold myself back from blocking the kick) our offense took the field for the first time.

In the huddle, with Thomas barking out the plays, I almost felt the way I would imagine a proud father does. The first play of his varsity career was a handoff to me, and I was going to make it memorable.

The play was designed to run through the A-gap between Caleb Clark, our right guard, and the center Zane Lewis, but the space closed so quickly that rather than running through my own players, I decided to unassumingly maneuver around them and run to the right of Noah Jeffries, the tight end. A Carrasco linebacker was squared up and charging straight for me as I turned the corner around Noah's hip, which likely would have been the end of the play for the majority of such scenarios, but I shrugged him off like you would a toddler trying to prevent you from walking through a doorway. The dull murmur of the crowd suddenly turned to raucous cheers as I averted the tackle, and I felt tingling goosebumps spread across the skin of my neck, back and forearms. I threw a stiff arm, keeping the next Pioneer defender at bay, but grabbing his jersey to keep him from flying through the air from my push. I dropped him as I felt him lose his balance, making it look like any other missed tackle, before taking two steps that were so unexpectedly fast for a "normal" human that it completely threw off the timing of two would-be tacklers, and instead of hitting me, they slammed into each other to the roaring approval of the fans. There was one defender left between me and the open green stretch sprawling toward the end zone, and all I had to do was outrun him. So I let him stay close enough to make people think he might catch me before pulling away by a step or so and trotting across the goal line.

I turned to look at the crowd on their feet and still screaming at a deafening decibel, as the band struck up *Hail Oak Hill!*

I was half expecting someone to come escort me off the field right then and there, wondering if maybe I hadn't been quite convincing enough, but no one that I saw seemed suspicious in any way. *If only they knew,* I thought. *This isn't football. This is acting.* I smiled as the thought sunk in, and I bowed with a flourish, like I had just delivered the performance of a lifetime.

One of the referees blew his whistle and tossed his yellow handkerchief into the air before signaling an unsportsmanlike conduct penalty, which forced our field goal unit to attempt the extra point from farther away, and Jeremy Dill, our kicker missed it short and wide to the right.

I thought an extra point was a small price to pay, even when they would have added up to a total of three by the end of the game. I was crafting each play of the game the way an artist carefully places each brush stroke of a painting, and the crowd, my team, and my coaches were all loving it. Three touchdowns, three bows, three penalties.

We won the game 32-10 and no one seemed to mind.

Elle and my mom met me, beaming, on the sideline after the game amidst a mass of other fans. I gave out more high-fives, and said "thank you" more times than I can remember.

The next day's *Oak Hill Press* front-page headline read, "Acorns Reap Talent Harvest in Rivalry Win."

I read that I'd finished the Carrasco game with 283 rushing yards on fourteen attempts, seventy-three receiving yards on four catches, two rushing touchdowns, a receiving touchdown (thrown by Thomas!), and the fifty-two-yard interception return for a touchdown.

Under the bold-lettered headline was a photo of me toting the ball during the interception and ensuing run.

I marveled at it.

The article vaguely recounted my heroics and was dotted with phrases like "herculean effort," and "the game of his life," and "obviously well-coached." I grinned as I read them. The reporter who interviewed me after the game, a middle-aged, balding man named Jimmy Dunham, asked me what I had done during the offseason to have come on so strong. I gave him some line about hard work and preparation, and I recognized it in the article. Apparently, he'd interviewed Briggs as well, because I read a quote talking about how much the Acorns' staff had prepared me over the offseason and how they had big plans for me heading into the rest of the year. The last line ended with, "Oak Hill could be in for a fruitful autumn, at least as far as football's concerned. And if last night was any indication, start getting used to the name 'JJ Morris.'" I put the paper down on our kitchen table that morning, feeling like I'd just eaten a four-course meal. Under Mr. Dunham's name were the words "Sports Editor."

"Just wait, Jimmy. Just wait."

I think I read that article four or five, maybe six times that day.

I couldn't stop looking at it. And the more I did, the more I wanted there to be another one.

There was a buzz at OHHS on Monday, after the first game that year. But each time I walked the hallways, or through the cafeteria, I heard the talking decrescendo to whispers. People I normally talked to a lot, or at least knew from class, just stared as I passed. It was as if, in one weekend, my athletic feats had catapulted my social status from recognized to revered.

Elle seemed extra snuggly when I saw her, and held my right arm with both of hers as we walked to class.

I realized quickly that my life had changed, but I wasn't sure what to do with it.

Finally, during one of my classes after lunch, I asked to be excused to go to the bathroom and saw Charlie in the hallway hanging up posters for some upcoming choir performance.

"What's gotten into everybody around here?" I asked.

"What do you mean?"

"No one will... talk to me." I felt like a whiny little boy as the words came out of my mouth.

"Oh, that..." she said smiling. "Well word on the street is that you're really good at football." I laughed and felt my cheeks flush.

"But, other guys have been good before," I said. "Cam got an offer from Minnesota. But I don't remember it being like this, or at least, I never noticed it."

"Yeah. Well, someone said *you* got offered a scholarship."

"A scholarship?"

"Yeah," she said. "Did you?"

"No." I was racking my brain, trying to remember back through the swirl of all the "congratulations," and "way to go, kid," and hugs I received after the game. Surely I would know if I'd been offered a college scholarship. “I don’t think so.”

“Oh,” she said. “Well, I thought it sounded like something my dad would’ve known. But Aiden said he heard there was a scout there.”

“Really?” I said, realizing I sounded more excited than I wanted to sound. I lowered my voice. “From where?”

Charlie laughed. It made me smile, even while I was desperate to know who it was that might have seen me play.

“I think he said Grand Valley? Or maybe it was SVSU…” she pondered aloud. I thought about Boogie and the way he’d talked about Grand Valley.

“Oh,” I said. There was an obvious lack of excitement in my voice.

“What?” she said.

“Well, those are just D-II schools.”

“Yeah, but it’s still college. My dad’s always excited when anyone gets an offer.”

“Yeah, I know,” I said. “I was just hoping for something a little more… I don’t know.”

“On TV?”

“Yeah!”

She smirked.

“Well, I didn’t mean…” I heard myself sounding like an arrogant prick as I replayed the conversation in my mind.

“No, it’s okay,” she said, laughing. “I understand. And besides, you *were* kind of incredible.”

Kind of incredible? I knew that what she called incredible was me trying to not be incredible, or at least not being as incredible as I was capable of, but still, the words cut through the façade and filled me with a sense of importance.

She must have seen my face betraying my amusement of the compliment. She giggled.

“Yeah, I was like, ‘Dang, I know him,’” she said. “I was super impressed.”

I lowered my head to hide my smile and the satisfaction I felt.

Charlie and I said our goodbyes, I told her I had to get back to class, and we parted ways. She turned to get back to hanging her posters, and I turned back the direction I'd come when I suddenly remembered I still hadn't gone to the bathroom. Just a few paces from where I'd left Charlie, I stepped through the entryway on my right that led into the boy's bathroom and proceeded to the middle of three urinals in the empty room. But that was when I heard a girl's voice quietly echoing into the tiled bathroom from the hall.

"Was that JJ?" the voice asked.

"Oh, yeah," Charlie said, over the sound of the shuffling poster.

"How's that going?" *Is that Rachel?*

"It's all right, it all just kind of sucks," Charlie said.

"Yeah," said Rachel. "I know."

I felt the rush of overhearing something juicy, like a jolt of energy down my spine.

"Well, why don't you just tell him how you feel?"

"How I feel?" Charlie said. "What do you think his girlfriend would say about that?"

"I mean, I saw you guys kiss. I was there, remember?"

My blood felt cold, and I had that rollercoaster big-hill-drop feeling in my stomach.

"What, that? That was just stupid. It was a game. It didn't mean anything. Well, probably not to him, at least."

"It didn't look like a game to me. The way he looked at you..."

"Stupid Mikey," Charlie said. There was a pause.

"Well I've got to go, but let's talk more later, okay?" Rachel said. "I'll see you in Art."

What just happened? I thought. The silence began to feel heavy in my ears as my thoughts soared. And then I realized I was still standing at the urinal.

28

Hank was waiting for me in the parking lot that day after football practice with an unabashed grin spread across his face. Normally, I caught a ride from Thomas, or used alternative methods to get home in a timely manner, but seeing as though my father had gone out of his way to come see me after nearly a year, I figured I'd throw him a bone.

He told me about how he'd read all about the game in the newspaper, and how he'd wanted to be there, but couldn't get out of work. He told me how he thought if I kept it up, there would definitely be college scouts wanting to talk to me. He told me I'd have to watch my back and make sure I knew who my real friends were, and that I'd have to watch out for the girls. Mind you, this was all during the five-minute drive to Taco Bell.

"I can just imagine you grabbing that ball and taking it—" he made an airy whistle and pointed his finger like a gun toward some imaginary end zone as we sat with nearly a mountain of tacos and burritos between us. "I mean, I was pretty fast, but it sounds like you're just on another level. Ol' Briggs got you on some weights or something?"

I laughed. "Yeah, or something."

His face suddenly turned a shade more serious. "What do you mean?" he said.

"I mean… I don't know. It's not Briggs."

He leaned in closer to me by the table's edge. "Steroids?" It was almost a whisper. "I know what goes on in football locker rooms man. I've been there."

"Uh, no."

"Because, hey listen, if you are—"

"I'm not, okay?"

"Okay, okay." He leaned back in his seat and started unwrapping another taco. "I just wanted to make sure. People usually don't just get good over one offseason like that, you know?"

"Are you saying I wasn't good last year?" I said with a grin.

He chuckled. "Well, that's not exactly what I meant. I'm just saying it sounds like you were *really* good on Friday."

We both laughed, and I shoved the last bite of a taco in my mouth and placed the crumpled paper wrapping onto the ever-growing pile next to my elbow. I promised myself that I would take at least a couple home for mom for dinner.

"So how's Allie?" Hank asked.

A streak of panic sliced through me. *How would he have known about the Rogers' house?*

"You mean Elle?" I said, bracing myself.

"Yeah, yeah. Sorry. Elle. How's she? How are you guys doin'?"

"It's all right," I said with a sigh. I took a huge bite of burrito.

"Just all right?"

"Yeah, pretty much," I said with my mouthful.

"What? You kids having trouble?"

"Well, no. I don't know."

"No? What do you mean?"

I shrugged, dismissively.

"Does your mom know about this?" Hank asked, looking around as if someone might overhear him.

"No, not really."

"Then you've *got* to tell me," he said with a sly grin. "I never hear anything first."

I laughed. "Well… It's not so much her."

Hank leaned in close, crossing his arms and resting them on the table.

"It's… I don't know. Things are just different. It was all fun at first, and now, I don't know, it's all just weird all the time."

"Don't I know how that goes."

"And…" I said. His eyebrow perked up, and he lifted his face slightly. "Well, there's kind of another girl, too."

"Another girl?" he said, with a sly smile. "Like what are we talking about here?"

"Well, nothing really. I just… I don't know."

"You've been driving this car a while, and now you just saw a bright shiny new one driving down the road?"

"Uh, yeah. Maybe?"

"I know, kid. Been there. And you know what I think?"

"What?"

"Drive 'em all."

"Really?" I said with a laugh.

"Yeah man. You're only in high school once. And then after that, you just never know where your life might end up." On the last few words his eyes got that faraway look, and he leaned back in his chair and picked up his paper cup and took a drink. "Well, *your* life will probably end up a whole lot different, at least I hope. I hope you'll have all the girls still chasing you around in college and maybe even after." He smiled. "You just keep doing what you did, and you'll be all right."

I broke up with Elle that night. On the phone.

Yes, I know I'm terrible.

But I just couldn't do it anymore. I didn't love her. We'd had fun. But I wasn't having fun anymore, and I should be having fun, right? At least, those were my thoughts as a senior in high school.

The last few weeks of our relationship were borderline miserable when we were together—at least they were from my perspective. She was pouring it on extra thick. I don't know if the previous events (namely, the one at Charlie's house) had anything to do with it, or if we just weren't on the same page, but every time she called me "baby" I cringed. When she hugged me and wouldn't let go, my skin squirmed. When she snuggled me on the couch while we watched a movie, I just wanted to move, and not be entangled in her sinking-sand grip. I was just annoyed by… everything.

I knew it wasn't fair, and I also knew the real reason behind all of it was rather obvious, because Elle knew it too.

"I know you like Charlie," she said outright between wet-sounding sniffles. And despite my vehement attempts to dissuade her, I could never bring myself to actually deny it.

Eventually, our conversation just devolved to me saying, "Listen, I'm sorry," and her saying, "Whatever," over and over again.

After what felt like a much longer time than I'm sure it was, we said our goodbyes.

"Goodnight, Elle."

"Goodbye, JJ."

And just like that I was a free agent.

I'll admit that I did feel bad about the whole thing, but what was a guy like me, in my position, to do?

I hardly slept that night (even by my standards), but it was more out of excitement than anything else.

The next morning, when I told my mom what had happened before school, all I got was, "Oh?" as she sipped her coffee and looked at me with raised eyebrows.

"Do you want to… talk about it, or anything?" she said after a few silent moments.

"I don't think so."

"All right," she said. "Well, did she cry?"

"Mom."

"Sorry. I'm just not all that sorry, I guess."

"Why?" I said. I thought *I* was supposed to be the calloused, heartless fiend here.

"I just didn't like the way she had her claws in you."

"Claws?"

"Look, I just didn't want a grandbaby sitting on my lap at your graduation."

"Oh God," I said, and dropped my head into my hands, laughing.

29

Thomas was a little surprised by the news of me breaking up with Elle when I told him at his locker at school the next day. He was more concerned about whether or not she "knew." I assured him she didn't.

"That's probably for the best," he said as he stuffed two of his textbooks into the small already-crowded space. "That's all we need—some crazy ex-girlfriend running around telling the cops about you."

"We?" I said, laughing.

"Yeah." He was laughing too. "I figure you're going to need some kind of agent or at least a butler or something."

"A butler?"

"Yeah, I want to come work at your mansion when you're rich and famous."

I laughed. "Yeah, okay. Well, maybe I could just get you your own place."

"No, no handouts," he said with a toothy grin, as he tried to contain a chuckle. "I don't believe in freeloaders." We both laughed. He slammed the locker door shut. "Okay, okay, but right now, we've got to make sure that we make it that far, and if Elle goes around telling everybody crazy things—"

"What are you girls laughing at?" It was Charlie. She'd walked up without us realizing she was there. She reached into the bag slung over her shoulder and pulled out a white Acorns football jersey—my jersey. "Elle, gave me this. Told me she didn't need it anymore."

I didn't know if I felt more embarrassed, knowing the point Elle was trying to make, or more stunned by her passive aggression.

"Did you guys break up?" Charlie asked.

"Yeah," I said.

"Oh, I'm sorry. What happened?"

I looked at Charlie, and then to Thomas. I hadn't even told him all the details of Elle and my parting of ways. I knew it probably wasn't the best time to get into particulars.

"Oh, it was just time," I said.

"Hmm..." Thomas said.

"Well, did she break up with you?"

"No," I said, quickly. "We just… I…"

"It's okay," Charlie said. "I guess we're just all part of the single's club now." She smiled and began to walk away. "Oh, and I guess you might want this to impress your next lady." She offered me the jersey.

"Well, you can…" I trailed off, blanking on anything else to say. I took the jersey from her.

30

By Friday's game, I had worked out a plan to talk to Charlie about the real reason I had broken up with Elle. It went something like this: be amazing during the game, confess the crush I had on her after the game while basking in the glow of victory. And then she would tell me she felt the same way. I know. Intricate.

The Acorns were hosting a team from Lansing that was supposed to be one of the premier teams in the state, and I knew the opportunity I had before me was prime, not only for my "plan," but also because of the other team's all-state running back that a bunch of scouts would be there to watch.

The game went as well as anyone in Oak Hill could have imagined, if not better. I ran for nearly 300 yards on the ground, caught five passes that went for another 100 yards or so, scored five touchdowns (three rushing, two receiving), and most importantly, fumbled once when the opportunity arose just so people wouldn't suspect anything, and I wouldn't look too perfect. We won 43-33, which was good too. Thomas threw one touchdown pass that wasn't to me on a play where Briggs used me as a decoy to draw a lot of defenders, and Josh Williams was literally waving his hand, all alone in the end zone. The all-state running back had a decent game, "...but it was JJ Morris who stole the show," as Jimmy Dunham wrote for the next day's paper. I knew I had gotten the job done when I saw Charlie waiting along the fence line, a little ways down from my mom and Thomas's family making their way down the stands to where the other fans usually stood waiting for the players to make their way over to them.

I also saw Coach Haines standing with two men—each one flanking him on either side—looking toward our huddle on the field. One wore a maroon golf polo with a yellow stylized "C" on the right side of his chest, with khaki pants, athletic shoes, and a baseball cap that matched his shirt. The other wore a dark jacket, with a green polo with thin horizontal white stripes poking out from beneath it. He wore khaki pants and black running shoes.

"And I don't know how he does it," Briggs said. "But JJ keeps saving our necks. Where'd you come from? Krypton?" All the guys laughed. "I'm going to give the game ball to Thomas just so your head doesn't get too big. Helluva game tonight boys. Hacksaw, break us down."

Hacksaw stood and everyone gathered around him with their helmets raised in one hand above their heads. He screamed something no one outside of the team would've understood, and got the guys riled up to answer his call-and-response chant of the words "Oak Hill" and then we broke the huddle.

I was about to make a beeline for Charlie when I felt a slap on my shoulder pad.

"JJ." It was coach Haines. "I was just talking to some scouts about you." Any thoughts I'd had vanished from my mind.

Haines told me they were from Central Michigan University and Michigan State University, and explained that they hadn't intended to come for me, but were so impressed with my athletic ability that they were interested in staying in touch through the rest of the season and said there was a chance I would be hearing from their head coaches if I kept playing like I had.

"Hell of a game, kid. Hell of a game." Haines slapped me on the back and started to walk back to where the other coaches were congregated, waiting for Briggs to finish talking to Jimmy Dunham.

I couldn't believe it. I mean, I knew that with my powers any school in the country would be grateful and lucky to have me on their team, but the realization that real live college football programs were taking notice of me suddenly made my lungs fill with excitement, and my chest spread with the warmth of satisfaction and imagination. This was actually happening.

Neither of those schools was very far from Oak Hill, so surely Mom would let me go, right? And once I was there, I could take the stage in an even more prominent venue. Heck, I'd probably be playing in the NFL pulling down all kinds of zeroes on the end of my paycheck within just two or three years! Could you imagine? Me—JJ freakin' Morris—a millionaire at age twenty?! What luck I'd had after all. Just a few months before I had been nervously waiting for the cops to show up and arrest me for smashing up someone's house and then ship me off to some government laboratory for testing, and now I was imagining myself walking across a stage to shake hands with some guy in a fancy suit as he announced me getting drafted into professional football. And then I'd be driving a Lamborghini and living in a mansion overlooking a beach somewhere. *If Boogie could see me now,* I thought. I still wasn't sure where these "powers" had come from, but boy was I glad I had them.

What would Hank say?

It was in that moment that I realized I was still standing on the field. I looked up to see Charlie waving at me.

Well, here goes nothing.

"JJ!" she said, and hugged me over the fence. "You did so good."

"Thanks," I said, shifting my helmet from one hand to the other. "Whew, what a game, huh?" I acted as if I had really been worried about the outcome.

"Yeah, crazy! Honestly, I didn't think you had a chance against those guys." I laughed. At least she was honest. "Hey, were those *scouts* over there?" she said with a wide-eyed expression.

I was so glad she'd noticed, but I tried to play it off like it was the most normal thing that had ever happened to me. "Uh... those guys? Oh, yeah, I guess they were."

"What?! Really? From where?"

"Um… Central and MSU."

"State?" she said. "That's Big Ten!"

"I know," I said. "Coach said they asked about me." I was trying to act cool and confident. Not like the giddy five-year-old that I felt was dancing around in my chest.

"That's awesome, JJ! That's just like what you were saying you wanted the other day."

"Yeah, I guess so," I said. I looked up and saw my mom talking to Thomas and his family. I knew it would only be a few moments before they saw us and walked our way, so anything I was thinking about doing would have to be fast.

"Listen," I said. "About my jersey—"

"Oh, don't worry about it. Elle gets a little… well, you know."

"Yeah, but… I want you to wear it," I said in a rush. The words felt like they floated in the air, not making their way to Charlie's ears in a hurry.

"Wear it?"

"Yeah. The reason she gave it to you is because she thought that I broke up with her because I like you. And, well…" The knot in my stomach twisted even further. "She's not wrong."

Charlie's eyes looked like they were reading a page of words that had been plastered onto my face. She wasn't smiling and I was suddenly very unsure of what to do next. The scenario in my mind's eye hadn't really made it into the finer points of this conversation.

"Wait, you broke up with Elle… for me?"

Finally we're getting somewhere.

"Well, yeah," I said. "I think I have for a while. Liked you, I mean."

"JJ," she said. "I'm flattered, really. And I like you. I think you're a really neat guy." *Oh lord, here we go.* "You're cool. But, I just got out of a relationship, and so did you. And… I don't know. It just doesn't feel like the right thing, right now. I'm afraid we'd be rushing into things. I… I'm sorry."

"Oh, well, I'm sorry. I thought…"

"No, no," she said, apologizing. "Please, let's just—can we still be friends?" I was wishing she would have taken away my powers and just punched me in the gut. I imagined it couldn't have felt any worse.

"Hey, there's that man!" It was Thomas, and he whacked my shoulder pad as he walked up to where we stood. "What you kids doing over here?" he said with a smug smirk.

"Oh, just talking," Charlie said, returning to her previously more excited tones. "JJ was just telling me about some colleges that were here."

"Colleges?" Thomas said.

"Yeah," I mumbled.

"Did you hear that, Ms. Morris? JJ said there were college coaches!"

"Two of 'em," Charlie added to Thomas.

"Two of 'em!" he yelled.

Thomas's family and my mom started to walk toward us.

"What's wrong, JJ?" Thomas said.

"Nothing."

"No, really, what's wrong man? If I just played the game that you did and knew there were scouts watching, I'd be thinking about what car I'm going to buy."

"Nothing, man. I'm just tired."

"Tired? *You're* tired?" Thomas gave me a look that asked more than his words did. Something like, "I know you're not tired because you have flippin' superpowers, dude. What is going on?"

But I just started to walk away. "Yeah," I said. "I'm tired."

I walked into school on Monday feeling pretty sorry for myself. Here I was, the star of the football team, quite literally a superhuman, a guy that any girl would be lucky to date, and a guy that even broke up with another girl—all for nothing.

I'd spent the majority of my weekend lying on the couch watching a smorgasbord of football, from college to pro to highlights of both on ESPN, and even some of my own game film, while taking breaks to play video games every now and then and, of course, eat snacks (I think I ate three bags of Doritos on Saturday alone). I even ignored Thomas's invitations to come hang out.

If my rise in popularity, football skills, and breakup didn't work, then what am I supposed to do to make Charlie like me?

Those were all the tools I had at my disposal.

The situation seemed dire.

And it was made worse by the fact that Thomas and Charlie were sitting next to each other in the cafeteria at lunch when I walked in. Normally, we'd sit and talk about our lives and football and the latest movies, but I just wasn't in the mood to go listen to them laugh and joke around with Charlie acting like nothing had happened. Thomas didn't even know about all of it, and who could possibly have told what kind of remarks he would make if he did.

No, I turned around and found the only open table I could on the perimeter of the cafeteria, out of sight from my friends, and hidden behind a brick column. It smelled even more strongly of school cafeteria food than the rest of the room because of its proximity to the small kitchen area where part-time employees were working feverishly to heat and serve stir-fry and "freshly baked" chocolate chip cookies.

I was just about to bite into one of the peanut butter and jelly sandwiches I had packed myself when a brown paper sack thudded down onto the table across from me. The bag belonged to Kiera Nash who was known as a "popular" girl in my grade that sometimes ran with the same crowd as Elle. She was, in nearly every guy in Oak Hill's opinion, very attractive and she knew it. She had a reputation that preceded her, that even some of the teachers and parents were keen to, which included a (reportedly lengthy) list of every guy she had ever made out with, and rumors of a second list that was, well, let's just say more in depth.

Kiera sat across from me wearing a friendly smile and a low-cut, tight shirt that left little to the imagination. We'd been in several of the same classes throughout high school, and had Ms. Henry's science fiction and fantasy literature class together at that time. But despite our shared experiences I had never really considered us to be friends.

"Mind if I sit here?" She laid her chemistry textbook and a red notepad down on the table beside her lunch.

"Uh... no, not at all," I said, trying to sound like I wasn't completely taken off guard. "Go ahead."

"Thanks," she said. "I really need to work on this chem homework, and I knew I wouldn't be able to if I sat with everybody."

"Yeah," I said. "I'm kind of in the same boat."

She opened the textbook and began rifling through the pages, looking for the right chapter. Once she found it, she pulled a pencil from the spiral binding of the notepad and noisily began turning the pages.

"I heard that Elle's moving," Kiera said after she'd jotted down a few notes in her notebook.

"Moving?"

"Yeah, isn't that why you guys broke up?"

"Well..."

"That's what she's been telling people. Her dad used to work for the police department down in Detroit and I guess they wanted him back."

"Oh, right," I said, nodding. "That."

I had no idea what she was talking about. Frankly, I didn't feel like setting the record straight even though I wanted to.

"Yeah," she said, perhaps picking up on my uncertainty. "Well, however it happened, you guys *are* broken up, right?"

"Yeah, of course."

"Oh okay. Well, I'm sorry," she said, looking me straight in the eyes. She broke her gaze and looked back at her textbook, tapping the eraser of her pencil on the notepad. "That paper for Henry's class is due next Monday, right?"

"No, it's this Friday," I said.

"Really?!" Her eyes snapped back to mine, horrified. "Oh gosh, I haven't even started on it."

"Really?"

"Yeah. And I have no idea what to write on."

"Well, there's tons of stuff to pull from in that movie," I said. "Just take Luke's belief that he was meant for something more than a simple life, or the way he talks about his dad to Ben. There's tons of identity stuff going on."

"See," she said, grinning. "I knew I sat here for a good reason. You probably already finished yours, huh?"

"Yeah, pretty much," I said.

"Gosh, you never seem stressed about any school stuff. I wish I was like that."

I chuckled. "Yeah, well I guess you could say it's a gift."

"Well, do you think you could share that gift with me?"

"Well," I laughed. She looked like she was waiting for an answer. "Uh, what do you mean, exactly?"

"I don't know, I just think you're good at writing papers and stuff and you seem to like that class. Maybe you could explain what that movie is about?" she said with a grin.

"Oh, yeah. I guess I could." I couldn't think of a good excuse not to. "You want to just meet up in the library or something? I've got a little time before football starts."

"Yeah," she said. "Or you could just come over after football. My dad will have the Tigers' game on, and you can help me write this thing."

I knew it wouldn't look very good. Anyone who found out about it would think I was on the rebound. But if Elle was moving, then maybe it didn't matter. Thomas would surely understand, although I was sure he would give me a hard time anyway. Elle might have a thing or two to say if she found out. At the very least, I reasoned that maybe it would at least make Charlie understand that I was on the market (and there were other buyers). And, if for no other reason, I didn't have any plans. It wasn't like I was imagining a future with Kiera. I'd always found her to be more of a nuisance than the goddess she was to other guys. But there I sat, with a cute girl who was not only asking me for my help, but also inviting me over to her house to watch sports. Those opportunities don't just happen all the time, at least not to me. And I thought maybe that was exactly the kind of thing I needed to get me past the emotional bludgeoning I had endured over the weekend. It seemed harmless enough.

"Will there be food?" I asked.

After I finished my lunch and told Kiera I'd see her later, I went to class wondering if what I'd decided was the smart choice, and whether or not I should tell anyone about it.

It rained terribly hard that Monday and thunder began to rumble early in the afternoon, so because of the fact that Coach had "planned" a light session anyway, football practice was moved indoors. After walking through a few new plays that Briggs thought would be a good addition to our scheme, he ordered us to hit the weight room.

I went through the motions of the workout Coach Haines had scribbled out on the big white board and then sat down at the end of one of the bench presses by one of the box fans that was churning out cool air amidst the warm, damp air of the weight room. Thomas was pushing through his last few reps of leg presses, and I was watching his scrunched face, beads of sweat sliding down his forehead and cheeks, glistening in the bright white of the fluorescent bulbs overhead, his leg muscles taught with exertion. And I thought about the effort it would take me to lift the weight he was struggling to move in his tired state. My mind started to wander back to Kiera Nash and how it had come to be that I was going to her house later that day. Other guys finished up their sets, re-racked their weights and began to slip out of the door in small clusters. My thoughts were interrupted when Haines plopped down on the bench beside me.

"What you doing, Jay?" he said.

"Nothing, coach."

"Are you done with the workout?"

"Yeah, I guess so."

"You guess so?"

"Uhh... yeah." It was unconvincing, but I was having a tough time saying I was done since I had hardly broken a sweat. Coach

Haines looked at me over his thick glasses in the way that I saw him look at people a lot—part grin and part scowl, so you couldn't tell if he was in a good mood or about to scream at you. He smiled.

"You ever heard of Blackjack Bill?" Haines asked.

"Was he... a pirate?"

Haines laughed.

"No. A football player. He was a quarterback."

"Blackjack Bill, huh?" I asked in a semi-mocking tone.

"Yeah. He was incredible. He could throw the out route like no one I've ever seen before. He he had a cannon of an arm. *And* he could run, you know? Run the way you want a running back to. People started calling him 'Blackjack' because some newspaper writer compared him to a hustler at a casino—seeming like he didn't have a clue when really he was always a step ahead." He laughed and I did too. "He had it, man."

"Well, what happened to him?"

"Laziness," he said. "Or selfishness is probably more accurate. He had so much God-given talent it wasn't even funny. Guys work their whole lives to get the chance to play college football, and this guy basically just showed up and had a spot. He spent way more time and energy picking up cute girls at parties than he ever did on his homework or his playbook, he showed up to practices with a hangover or worse, and he acted like he was some sort of Hollywood celebrity." Haines paused and looked out over the weights and racks in front of us. "Eventually he stopped being able to scramble his way out of every bad read and the coaches sat his ass on the bench. It wasn't too long after that he would've gotten pulled anyway because he didn't have the grades. His work ethic..." Haines shook his head like he was seeing it all right in front of his eyes. "Just goes to show you, you can have all the ability in the world, but if you don't want it, if you refuse it, it won't stick around and wait for you. Instead of college ball, one of the most promising young quarterbacks I've ever seen was working the checkout at a gas station. It broke my heart."

We sat in silence for a minute.

"You know what Jay?" Haines said in a grim tone. He adjusted his position on the the bench next to me. "I see a lot of ol' Blackjack in you."

My stomach sank.

He was calling me out.

"I see some of that slacking off, cutting a corner here or there, that attitude toward anything that isn't going be 'fun' that says it's not worth your time."

I wanted to defend myself; to tell him he was wrong, and to tell him why. But I couldn't find the words.

"But, I can deal with all of that," he said with a subtle wave of his hand. "Because I can see greatness too. You're a good kid—a special young man. It's obvious that you were meant for a lot more than high school football. And you don't have to end up at a gas station. In fact, I don't want you to, and I'm going to do everything I can to make sure that doesn't happen."

Wow, I thought. There was a sense of pride—no, of determination—spreading through my chest, and I felt a lump welling up in my throat. I swallowed hard. *What's wrong with me? Guys aren't supposed to do this.*

"So, tomorrow morning? Let's say five o'clock, right here. What do you say, Mr. Morris?"

33

I walked across the damp high school parking lot after that workout with the rain still drizzling from the heavy grey clouds overhead.

My father telling me he was proud of me over tacos a few weeks earlier had felt like it was supposed to be some kind of an important moment. And while I appreciated his words, it had come on the heels of a football game in which I had used superpowers to my significant advantage. Part of me wanted to believe that my dear old dad had finally come around, but the other part of me wasn't so sure I should even get my hopes up. This was Hank after all.

But no one had ever used the word "greatness" when they were talking about me. And no one had ever said much about my prospects of a successful life beyond high school. I mean, sure, my mom had told me she hoped I went to college someday and that she "knew I could do it," and wanted me to get a good job, and have a beautiful family, and give her grandbabies and all that. But, I'd never heard anyone talk about my future the way that Coach Haines had. I didn't think he even suspected what made me different from all the other football players he'd seen—even Blackjack. But his words filled my head and my heart with a sense of something bigger than what I knew of my life in Oak Hill, as if maybe all of this actually added up to something significant. Something like destiny.

Greatness.

I could feel the lump in my throat coming back.

I coughed into the sleeve of my sweatshirt. Guys weren't supposed to do this. Especially not football players. And especially, *especially*, not people with superpowers.

A car pulled up next to me and the window rolled down.

"You want a ride Mr. Kent? Or are you flying today?" It was Thomas and a couple of the offensive linemen, Zane and Caleb, in the back. It always caught me a little off guard when he said stuff like that in front of other people, but no one ever said anything that made it sound like they suspected anything other than that "Superman" might be my nickname on the football field.

I laughed as I climbed into the passenger's seat.

"You all right, man?" he said quietly as he looked at me now sitting just a few feet away. He looked concerned.

"Yeah," I said, before clearing my throat. "I'm good. I'm good."

"You sure?"

"Yeah. What are we doing? T-bell?"

Thomas gave me one more look trying to decipher my truthfulness, and then put the car in drive.

"Yeah, man," Zane said. "I could go for about three burritos right now."

The conversation shifted to how we would fare in Friday's game and how much each of us had lifted in the day's workout.

It wasn't until we were almost to Taco Bell that I remembered I was supposed to go to Kiera's.

It took a few minutes, but eventually I removed myself from all of the jokes and comments I was getting from Thomas and my football buddies in the Taco Bell parking lot. Before I left, Thomas asked if I needed a ride with a knowing look, probably just for appearances. I told him I would jog it.

Kiera Nash's house was roughly two and a half miles from where we were. If you took the back roads it was probably over three, but that's what I did. Dashing out from behind trees after I'd made sure no one was watching, and then scrambling to the next cover I could find, I made my way to Kiera's front door in a matter of about ten minutes. I slowed to a walk once I made it into the subdivision where her house was, just to be as unassuming as possible.

She answered the door almost as I began knocking.

"Hey," she said with a smile. She was wearing different clothes, although not sweats or something comfortable that people like to change into when they're done working for the day. She wore a fresh shirt, and I was immediately confronted with the scent of perfume.

"Are we going somewhere?" I said, examining the sweatshirt and gym shorts I still sported from my workout.

"Oh, no," she said, crinkling her eyebrows like I'd asked an absurd question. "Come on in."

The Nash's house wasn't anything lavish, but it was charming and well-decorated with a few framed pieces of art you'd find at a craft store, and school portraits of Kiera and her younger brother, Hunter, hanging on the walls.

As promised, Kiera's dad sat in a recliner in their living room with the Tigers' game in progress on the large TV in front of him.

"Dad, this is JJ Morris," Kiera said.

"JJ, how are you, son?" he said. It almost sounded rehearsed. Almost.

"I'm good, sir," I said.

"Listen to this guy," he said. "Call me Scott." He looked up over the back of his chair. "Where's Hunter?"

"I think he's upstairs," said a female voice from the kitchen. Scott got up and excused himself and muttered something about "his favorite player," as he walked out of the room.

Kiera looked at me and smiled. A moment later a woman, probably in her early forties, entered the room wearing red lipstick, an autumn-yellow sweater, and an apron around her waist covering her dark jeans. Her hair was up in a messy, but intentional looking up-do, and she smiled widely, showing off a pearly white set of teeth.

"JJ, it's so nice to meet you," she said, and leaned in, giving me a hug. "I'm Kiera's mom, Trisha. We're so happy to have you over."

The whole thing was starting to feel a bit overdone. I had planned for baseball and homework, not Thanksgiving at the Nash's.

Hunter bounded into the room, and stopped a few feet from me, wide-eyed. He looked to be a year or two shy of ten, and sidled up next to his mom as I met his doe-eyed gaze.

"Do you know who that is?" Mrs. Nash asked. Hunter nodded.

"What's up, man?" I said.

"Hey," he said in a quiet voice.

"Do you play football?" I asked. He nodded again.

We chatted for a few minutes about peewee football, which was mostly me asking yes or no questions and him nodding or shaking his head. After what felt like much longer than it probably was, Kiera's mom told Hunter to say goodbye and ushered him out of the room. She came back a few minutes later with chicken pot pies on small plates for me and Kiera.

We sat watching the Tigers blow their 3-1 lead and ate amidst the sounds of metal forks scraping porcelain plates and Kiera's parents peppering me with questions about football, my future, and my home life. I felt more like I was interviewing for a job than coming over to do homework.

Eventually, Kiera told her parents we had things to do, and that I didn't come over to hang out with them. Her mom said it was time they started getting ready for bed anyway, what with Scott having to get up early for work and her having to get up and get the kids out of the house. With that, they disappeared up the staircase, and we were alone in the living room.

Kiera went to the kitchen, turned off the light, and came back with her backpack. She slung it down on the floor with a thud and crouched down beside it. Rummaging through the bag's contents she sighed and then said, "So, I started writing a little something, but I'm not sure if it's any good." She pulled two sheets of notebook paper free with some bubbly-looking handwriting on it and offered it to me. "Maybe you should take a look."

I took the papers and moved from my perch on the sofa so I could sit with my legs stretched out in front of me and my back against the firm cushions of the couch.

I read:

Star Trek is a great coming of age tale about a young boy who uses his wit and will to escape the clutches of his overbearing uncle who clearly represents the theme of disillusionment . . .

I tried really hard not to snicker, as I read "Star Trek," and then fought to stay quiet as I skimmed through the next few paragraphs about Luke's "interpersonal battle," and how he was really just looking for love.

I was starting to wonder if we'd even watched the same movie.

Kiera moved past me and sat down next to me on my right, and leaned back on the couch behind us staring up at the ceiling while she waited for me to finish reading.

I trudged on through a few more paragraphs that attempted to expound on a plot synopsis based on the initial musings, and then several ponderings on what role the robots even had to play in the whole thing. All of it was shocking.

Finally, I set the papers down, trying to figure out where even to begin with my feedback.

"Well, Elle was right," Kiera said.

"About what?" I turned to look her in the eyes.

"You."

I had no idea what Elle had said about me. Hopefully nothing too terrible. Kiera smiled and shifted her weight so she was turned toward me, resting on her hip with her arm propped up on the couch. "You're really cute when you read."

"I . . . what?" I said.

She nodded. "I can't believe she ever let you go."

"Well, she didn't really."

"Oh?" she said. Her smile shifted slightly and there was suddenly a wildness in her expression. "If you were my boyfriend, I'd make sure you never thought about letting go."

She leaned toward me and closed her eyes, pressing her lips against mine.

What is happening?! I thought. But I did nothing to resist. Despite my abilities, I was so taken off guard by what was taking place that I felt like I couldn't move. But deep down, it all felt off, like a bike chain that's come off its gear.

"Whoa! Whoa!" Light from the kitchen suddenly poured into the room, and there stood Scott in a navy-blue bathrobe. "Kiera, I think homework time is over," he said.

I could feel my face flush with warmth.

As I gathered my things to the sounds of Kiera telling her dad about how embarrassing it all was, and that she didn't need him telling her how to live her life, I could feel the urgency in his words as he responded, waiting for me to leave.

"Kiera, go upstairs. We'll talk about this later."

She stomped off with a grumble.

I quickly headed for the door, as fast as I could go without tipping off my special abilities.

"Now hold on just a second there," Scott said.

As I stepped onto the porch I turned to face him.

"Look, Mr. Nash, I—" He held up a hand.

"I know how these things go, JJ," he said. "You're a big football star. She's a pretty girl. But let's just not get carried away on the first date. You've both got futures to think about."

"I know," I said. "But—"

"Goodnight, JJ."

He shut the door.

I stood there stunned. *What just happened?*

As if to emphasize his point, I heard the lock latch.

34

I'm sure five o'clock was meant to feel early, but I woke up at 2:30 a.m., made myself a half-dozen scrambled eggs and some peanut butter toast, while I pondered the previous night.

Shouldn't I have known something weird was going to happen with Kiera? I mean, did I want something to happen? *Definitely not,* I told myself. *Definitely not.*

I walked into the gym at 4:57 and acted like I'd just rolled out of bed. High school seniors typically haven't already been up for hours and made themselves a hearty breakfast before five in the morning unless they're up to no good. Coach Haines said, "Good morning," and then I pretended to work out with him for the next hour and a half.

Don't get me wrong, he did a great job trying to coach me and give me pointers about technique, but the weight on the racks made me feel like I was lifting a cardboard box filled with packing peanuts.

"Do you think I'm ready for Friday?" I asked as we began re-racking all the weights.

"Honestly, after what I've seen from you lately, I think you're ready for about any game," Haines said. "But, you know, none of this is about getting ready for football games. This (he gestured to the room) is about the rest of your life, because life is way, way more than wins and losses on Friday nights, or Saturdays, or Sundays."

By the end of the day, I was glad to have gone to the lifting session. It, at least, gave me something else to think about.

To say *I* was confused by what had taken place at the Nash's home would've been one thing.

Unfortunately, that was only the beginning.

Word got out that I had been to Kiera's house. I'm still not sure if it was one of the football guys who talked, or if Kiera told someone, but somehow they all knew when we got to class the next day.

A few days later there were rumors going around that we had messed around and I got thrown out of her house wearing nothing but a bed sheet. Even Thomas asked me about it at one point, although he was quick to believe me when I told him what had really happened. I managed to convince several people that nothing had happened, but it wasn't enough to turn off the firehose of lies. Everywhere I went there were people regarding me differently than they had just days before. Girls looked at me with varying degrees of disgust, while guys acknowledged me in a range of expressions that spanned from admiration to disappointment.

In the span of a few days I had done for my "popularity" what had taken me years to do with my athletic feats, even with the aid of my unordinary abilities.

Though I had never wished for popularity in this way, and the first days of it were miserable, my reputation as a "bad boy" felt like it carried some sort of weight that I hadn't had before. After the next football game, in which I again starred, the glances that had previously been judgmental and full of disdain changed to be much friendlier after another convincing win.

By the middle of the next week, the clouds of the storm seemed to be parting, and it felt that at any moment the sun would be shining down on me again only with more fervor and favor than before. But there was one cloud that wouldn't budge—the feeling I got every time my eyes met Charlie's. It wasn't that she was looking at me with judgement, or even that she scowled and made mean faces. In fact, most of the instances that I saw her during that time she was smiling and laughing just like the Charlie I'd always known. The problem was that behind the smile, there was something buried deep down under the sparkle in her eye. And though I never saw it for long, as

I would look up in class, or suddenly become aware of her in the hallway, or even from across the table in the cafeteria, I would see a subtle flash—a glimmer really—of hurt.

You know those classes in school that you take because you have to have an elective in your schedule like P.E., home ec, or something with computers? The actual coursework takes you all of about five minutes of class time and then the rest of the hour you goof off and try not to get detention. Career Navigating was that for me my senior year. It was a random collection of about thirteen students from every class other than freshman, learning about everything from what careers might best suit our skillset to how to dress for a job interview. Our instructor was Mrs. Baker who also served as the OHHS librarian. Apart from giving us some initial instruction we didn't hear much from her. She would give us the daily assignment from the end of two rows of computers set in the middle walkway of the library with several aisles of bookshelves on either side. After the day's instructions, Mrs. Baker would then take up her post at the library's front desk, leaving us to our work and subsequent play.

Most of the time I just talked to Charlie. It was one of three classes we had together, but the only one that didn't include any of our other friends. And so it felt like just the two of us. How I had looked forward to 9:15 a.m. on Tuesdays and Thursdays.

But the days that followed the night at Kiera Nash's house made Car-Nav uncomfortable. I think both of us wanted to talk about it, or at least acknowledge it. I know I did. But neither of us ever brought it up. Instead, we just marched on dutifully, taking all of the career placement quizzes and researching college rankings for schools we knew we'd never attend. We talked, albeit mostly about school and occasionally football when she'd tell me something her dad had said. She knew I was lifting some mornings with her dad, and she asked how that was going, to which I always replied, "really good." And that was pretty much how things went. Painful. Drab. Emotionless. And nothing like how a guy wants things to go with any girl—especially one he thinks he might love.

35

Adam Albertson played on the football team every year that I can remember. He stood all of about five feet and seven inches, and probably weighed 130 pounds on his best day. He was quiet and mild-mannered, and he wasn't much of an athlete. But he worked hard, took direction well, and had earned the respect of the coaches and a spot on the team. It didn't hurt that the guy was practically a genius. He was taking college math courses as a sophomore, and now that he was a senior, the rumors going around were that he had only applied to Harvard. No one thought he'd need to look anywhere else.

But absent from his list of accolades, and nothing he'd learned whilst accumulating his immaculate grade-point average, was how to throw a punch—or, more importantly, block one. And on the Thursday morning after the week of Kiera-JJ rumors, that was exactly what he needed to know.

Apparently, Adam's younger brother, Brent, who was a freshman at the time, had accidentally collided with a senior—a brute named Chad—between classes in the hallway, and made him drop his open bottle of Mountain Dew between the library and the math and science wing—a busy student traffic area with few classrooms nearby. Chad, seemingly not possessing the vocabulary to express his dismay, had hauled off and shoved Brent into a locker, which Adam saw from about 100 feet away and came charging to his brother's aid.

We had convincingly won another football game over the weekend and led by so many points by halftime that Briggs had benched the starters for all of the fourth quarter and Adam had actually gotten to play on defense. I'm not sure if that was what had instilled extra confidence in him or if he would have done it anyway, but he basically tackled Chad. The problem was that Chad, although he didn't play any school sports, was the naturally strong and burly type, and no matter what amount of lifting or training Adam had done, no contests of strength between the two would have favored the wiry football player.

Of course, when Adam charged down the hallway and left his feet to take down another student, everyone came running and circled around the action. Naturally, that didn't include any responsible adults.

I had seen a few fights in school before. One I particularly remember was in middle school between two of the popular kids right after lunch. They traded a few punches in their name-brand collared shirts and then a teacher came and yelled and gestured wildly and wrestled them away from each other.

What I saw as Thomas, Zane and I hustled to the edge of this crowd was no fight. It was a beating. There was blood on Adam's grey sweatshirt that he'd wiped from his lip. He stood between Chad and Brent, fists raised. Adam swung at Chad's head, but Chad caught Adam's hand mid-swing, gritted his teeth, and clocked him across the face with his other hand. Adam crumpled to the ground next to Brent who looked helplessly at his brother. Most people probably would've looked to see if Adam was all right, but instead I was watching Chad—observing the slick sweat on his forehead and the savage gleam in his eye. And then I watched him take an ill-meaning step toward the Albertsons and something inside of me sparked.

This isn't right.

I dropped my backpack to the floor and strode forward in an instant. Before anyone knew what was happening, I had spun the punk around, grabbed him by the throat and lifted him a few inches off the ground with the intent of slamming him through the lockers. The clamor of the crowd rose in approval, but through it, I heard Thomas's voice.

"JJ!"

And I knew in that moment that if I did what I intended, I would kill this kid. Crushed windpipe. Snapped spinal cord. Something. He would be dead, or dying, and there would be a few dozen kids who had witnessed me become a monster.

I let go, Chad fell to the floor, and it all might have looked like I just awkwardly pushed him.

I looked at Thomas, who mouthed "Whew," and I saw Charlie standing behind him with an expression I couldn't quite read on her face.

It was then the teachers rushed in. They broke up the crowd and then whisked me, Adam, Brent, and Chad to the principal's office.

36

We lost our next football game 21-17—our first defeat of the year. I did what I could, but there's only so much that screaming and jumping around can contribute, even if you *do* have extraordinary abilities.

My "fight" with Chad earned me a two-day suspension from school, and ineligibility for that Friday's game. For the record, Chad got suspended too, and so did Adam.

My mom wasn't very happy about the whole ordeal, especially because she got the news in the middle of a long shift at the hospital. Principal Cook called her. But after we talked about it that night, and she heard my side of the story, she was less frustrated with me and more with the idea that school administration felt the need to suspend two students acting in defense.

The best thing that came out of it was that it all but erased the incident with Kiera. No one made any mention of me and her together after the fresh juicy news of the fight. It seemed to restore my standing and a sense of normality to my life.

When I saw Briggs after the game, he walked straight over to me, grabbed me by my shoulders and said, "I need you to stop being some kind of justice-seeking do-gooder and start getting your dumbass in gear to help this team. We need you on the field, not picking fights with low-life bullies. If you're not out there, none of these pansies look like they know what they're doing. And if you cost us another game this year—"

We both turned to look and see Thomas, who had just walked up to us, standing there, sweat and dirt streaked across his face and jersey, holding his helmet at his waist. He'd heard what Briggs had said. Without a word, he shook his head and then silently walked to the locker room.

I felt bad for Thomas. He wasn't a star quarterback, but he honestly wasn't bad. They'd almost won without me—a detail that was true largely because of him and Hacksaw—but Briggs couldn't let the loss go. Since I had earned a reputation on the field, he was becoming greedy, and it was taking its toll on the other players. Guys were starting to dislike me, just because Briggs wouldn't ever shut up about me. It was like I was his ticket to something more than just being the unknown coach of a historically bad high school football program. But Thomas kept a good attitude for the most part. He knew what was really going on, and no matter how coy Briggs thought he was or brash he acted in the locker rooms, Thomas could let all of the backhanded insults and constant grilling go, because he knew what Briggs did not. He knew the real me, and the fact that I was having to *try* to play football like a normal person, and how all of Briggs's strategizing and fretting over plays and schemes meant nothing because there was a superhuman freak of nature on his team that was doing things that weren't part of any game plan.

I saw Charlie waiting for her dad at the foot of the grandstand and was just formulating an idea of what I might go say to her when Briggs grabbed my arm.

"Don't worry about Winters, JJ. Don't worry about anyone or anything, except being on this field. Nothing else matters for you. You got it?"

"Nothing else matters," I said, no longer looking him in the eye. "Got it."

I headed toward the locker room.

It was the middle of the night, and Thomas and I were walking through the field by the barn I had accidentally destroyed the year before. I was telling him about that night and how bad I felt about the Rogers' house. It was the first time I could remember ever talking to him about it so openly, and as I was laying out all of the guilt I felt about it, we heard footsteps crunching through the snow behind us.

We both turned and saw a shadowy figure moving in our direction.

"So, it *was* you." It was a girl's voice.

"I, uh…"

"No it's okay. I knew it all along." She stepped closer and I felt the back of my neck tingle and beads of sweat beginning to form at the base of my hairline. It was Allie Rogers. "You thought you got away with it, didn't you? You thought no one would ever find out." Her stare bored its way through my eyes, down to my core. "I know who you are—who you *really* are."

Dread welled up inside of me.

I heard the sound of multiple sirens and saw the flicker of blue and red light dancing across the field around me. I looked back up to see half a dozen police cars screeching to a halt at various jagged angles in the road behind Allie. But it wasn't Allie anymore. It was Charlie.

"I KNOW WHO YOU ARE!"

I turned to run.

But there standing before me, was… me.

And I looked pissed.

What?

If it had been anyone else, I would have run around them or pushed them over or something. But knowing what I was capable of, I knew I couldn't just overpower or outrun me. I had, quite literally, met my match. Thomas was there standing off to the side, looking back and forth between the two JJs with his mouth agape. Then, the me I was looking at grabbed my shirt just below the collar with lightning-quick agility. Before I had time to react he reared back with a balled fist and gritted his teeth. I could see the lights from the police cars glowing in his eyes.

I braced for the blow.

I woke up in a panic, with blue and red lights flashing across the wall of my bedroom through the window, and sweat dripping down my forehead. As I got my bearings, I looked out the window that faced our neighbors house, and peered toward the street where I saw two police cars sitting next to two cars that had apparently bumped into each other on our quiet road.

I sat down on my bed trying to come to grips with the fact that there weren't two of me, and Allie Rogers, or Charlie for that matter, didn't *actually* know who I was. But still, I couldn't quite pull myself away from the emotions that I had felt so strongly just moments before.

My breath slowed, and I could feel my pounding heart begin to calm in my chest.

My mind, however, continued to race, and my thoughts turned to what would really happen if Allie ever found out.

My dream had injected me with a fresh dose of fear that I would be found out and then shipped off to a laboratory for testing.

Or worse.

I had become somewhat lax with my abilities, and let my success on the football field lure me into a feeling of comfort and ease.

The dream made me redouble my efforts to keep my secret hidden; using my powers to a lesser extent and trying to avoid conversation with Thomas about them.

It all made me nervous.

But all of that was pushed to the back of my mind during Career Navigating on the Tuesday I came back from being suspended for the fight with Chad. Charlie put her bag down and took her seat next to mine, muttering something to the effect of, "Well look who it is," sarcastically under her breath. I wasn't sure, but I felt like I could hear a different tone in her voice that hadn't been there the last time we'd spoken. It took me by surprise. She met my eyes with a genuinely kind smile.

I remember that I was taking a new career placement quiz online, and the question I was on was "Do you like to paint?" I had just been wondering why a career placement website would want to know why I painted when I was interrupted by that smile and the warm tone in Charlie's voice. She'd taken her seat, but still hadn't turned on her computer.

"Looked like the guys really missed you out there on Friday, huh?"

"Oh, yeah," I said. "I guess."

"Well, Coach (that's what she called her dad when we were talking football) said the team is really missing something when you're not out there."

"Oh," I said, thinking back to Briggs's comments after the game, before I realized the relayed compliment. "Did he really say that?"

"Yeah," she said, laughing. "But I disagree." She smiled, suddenly smug. I loved it when she smiled like that. "Who's going to bring everyone water if you're not on the bench?" She busted into an even harder laugh than before.

I grinned a weird toothy grin without meaning to. I couldn't help it.

"I do appreciate it when the water is distributed the right way," I said. "Maybe I've been chasing the wrong thing this whole time."

"I think you're right," she said, and gestured to my computer screen. It read, *93% Career Match: Sign Painter.* "I think you could have a long, illustrious career as a sign painter."

"Wow," I said. "You know, I'd never even considered that as an option. Talk about getting famous..."

"Instant celebrity" she said, almost unable to contain her snickering as Mrs. Baker looked up over the rim of her glasses from her desk.

I couldn't help but smile.

It was right before the bell rang to dismiss the class that Charlie looked at me with the traces of humor fading from her eyes, and said, "Listen... I don't... Do you want to come over for dinner?"

I don't know if I've ever been as nervous for a meal as I was that evening at the Haines' house.

I'd agreed to an early dinner the next Sunday, at 4:30 p.m.

Thomas was gone for the weekend visiting his grandparents in Indiana, and I hadn't told him about the dinner anyway. My mom was working shifts on Saturday and Sunday morning that weekend, and it was our bye week for football, so I'd had plenty of time to sit around and think about how nervous I was.

It took much more of my concentration than I'd like to admit to keep myself from visibly shaking as I walked to the door and knocked (gently, so I wouldn't smash a hole in it). But the warm aroma of a pot roast greeted me in the entranceway a few minutes after four when my mom dropped me off. Gosh it smelled good, which helped calm my knotted stomach as I walked in. Charlie's mom, Kelly, had prepared the roast with small red potatoes and carrots, and dinner rolls, with some butter set out in a fancy-looking glass dish. There were folded cloth napkins on each of the white plates, with shiny cutlery and glass goblets set out at each place setting. I had only ever seen anything like it around holidays when my grandma had us over for what she called a "proper meal." The fact that Coach Haines was watching football from his recliner with his feet up made me wonder if Thanksgiving Day had come early.

We talked about football, of course, but also a few stories about Charlie's younger years that made her roll her eyes, Coach and Mrs. Haines' dating stories (to which Charlie rolled her eyes many times as well), and my plans for college which weren't very complicated.

"I'm pretty much interested in whoever's interested in me at this point," I said.

We talked through specifics on a few of the schools I'd heard from, mostly small division IIs and IIIs, but several notable D-I schools that included Louisville, Western Michigan, and Toledo.

It was during cleanup when Mrs. Haines ordered me not to help, that Coach and I stepped outside and were talking alone on their back patio.

"I want to put the extension on the garage coming back out this way," he said, gesturing with one hand as he held a steaming cup of decaffeinated coffee in the other. "We'll be able to put both of our cars in and out of the snow when we need to."

"Oh yeah," I said. "That's a good idea." Coach nodded and then coughed into his free hand. Something caught my attention and I looked to see Charlie smiling at me from the other side of the glass door that led back into the house, near the kitchen.

"Hey, about college," Coach said after a moment, pulling me back from his daughter's attention. "I know a guy down in Toledo. You should have told me you were going to reach out to them. We used to play together back in high school."

"I didn't," I said.

"Didn't what?"

"Reach out to them."

"You mean you haven't been sending out a tape?"

I shook my head.

"To anyone?"

"Nope."

"Not even letters?"

"I don't think so."

"Hmm..." Coach pondered. "That's strange." He sipped his coffee. "I mean you've been having a great year, but... I'll have to look into—"

Coach coughed again.

And then again.

It was a phlegmy, rattling cough, and he covered his mouth with his forearm.

"Excuse me," he said, reaching up to fix his glasses.

He coughed again.

And then he bent slightly and spit, and we both looked down to see a scarlet splotch of sputum sitting on the sandy-colored wood of the porch. I glanced at the door and saw that Charlie was nowhere in sight.

"Don't worry about me," Coach Haines said. "I had a bad cold a while back, and this cough seems to keep hanging on. But it's nothing. I'll be as good as new pretty quick."

I left dinner that night with the image of Charlie beaming a smile at me as I climbed into her dad's pickup truck.

"I'll take good care of him," he'd said to Charlie with a wink, loud enough for both of us to hear. "Don't worry."

We talked about football, of course, and school, the chemistry quiz I hadn't studied for, whether the Detroit Lions had any shot of making the playoffs—all in the twelve minutes it took to get from the Haines's country home to my mom's house in Oak Hill.

As we pulled up to my driveway, the soft yellow glow of the living room light beaming through the front window, Coach Haines snugged the truck up against our tree-lined curb, shifted into park, and relaxed in his seat with his left arm loosely draped over the top of the steering wheel.

"Charlie likes you a lot, JJ."

I'd heard enough stories of dads putting unsuspecting guys through the ringer when it came to dating their daughter. Was this a test? My thoughts were swirling. I didn't know how to proceed.

"She does?"

He gave me a warm grin. "Yeah, she does. And I think you know that."

"Yeah," I said.

"Is the feeling mutual?" he asked.

I nodded. "Yes sir. Charlie's not like other girls."

"Ah, well… I hope that's a good thing."

"It is," I said. I paused not knowing if I was about to cross a line. "I think I… Well, I really, *really* like her." My relationship with Coach

Haines was complicated. At times I thought of him purely as coach, and at others he felt more like a friend. Sometimes he seemed to be a counselor. Sitting in his truck that night, he felt like a father. And so, looking back, I can see how telling a girl's dad that you have serious feelings for his daughter before ever broaching the subject with said girl might seem counterintuitive. But, talking to Coach Haines made me feel like I wanted his affirmation. Were these feelings for this girl valid? Was this just a passing whim of a seventeen-year-old boy? I was always afraid that Zane and Caleb or any of the other guys—heck, even Thomas—would just laugh, and then ceaselessly pick on me for a statement like that.

Coach Haines laughed.

"Is that right?"

I laughed, a little embarrassed by my own boldness.

"Well," he said. "She's my daughter, you know? So I don't know if I'll ever really get used to the idea of her hanging around a boy—especially a jock like you." He laughed again. And then he got a faraway look in his eye as he stared down the street. "She'll always be my little girl. Always..." He grinned and looked at me over the top of his thick gleaming glasses. "But, she's not so little anymore."

"JJ," he said. "You're a good guy. Just be honest with her. Don't rush things. And keep in mind you have your whole lives ahead of you. You never know what life's got for you around the corner."

Just be honest, I thought.

We said our goodbyes, and I stood on the sidewalk and watched his truck disappear into the night.

41

I felt like my life had been too good to be true.

Football was a breeze. The crowds of people cheering me on were fantastic, and seeing my name in the paper was fun. The games weren't hard and were the highlight of every week. Practice, even the sessions we had in the pouring rain or bitter cold and snow, were mind-numbing for someone who could outrun cars and jump over barn roofs. And even tests at school seemed to be easier, since I had more time to study and felt like I could remember everything I saw teachers write on white boards, or whole pages I'd read in textbooks. It was like all I had to do was open a drawer full of files in my mind and I could recall anything I'd ever seen.

Now, you'd probably think that all sounds great, and it was. At first. But, after so many days of pretending easy things were hard, just so I'd fit in, life got boring.

Until I started writing.

Ms. Henry, good looks aside, was a great teacher. She had a way of taking ordinarily boring things, like Shakespeare, and poetry, and just school in general, and making them sound like the most exciting thing in the world.

"We've put a man on the moon, we've cured hundreds of diseases, we've invented the internet," she'd said one day. And then she looked around the room, her eyes meeting each student's pupils. "All the great and unexplored worlds that lay ahead will be found here." She held up a white piece of paper.

It was this kind of thing that really kindled my curiosity.

I could memorize numbers or facts—I could practically recite anything I read. But writing was different. Writing required something of me that none of my special gifts could aid. There was no feat of strength or speed needed. Whether it was a paper about *The Count of Monte Cristo* or my own creations, there wasn't anything I could fake, and I loved it. Writing was real, and it probably would've become my escape to normalcy and freedom if that role hadn't been taken by a girl.

When we were both about seven, I remember giddily huddling under a table with Charlie in the cafeteria at church summer camp. The air was muggy and smelled like camp spaghetti and two-day-old garlic bread as it swirled around the room on the airwaves of a lazy box fan. But I didn't care.

We were playing hide-and-go-seek on a rainy day, and only the cafeteria, the tabernacle, and the indoor recreation room were in play. Somehow, we were the only two kids that chose to hide in the cafeteria, and both dove under the same plastic tablecloth at the same time. But just as we'd realized our mistake of giving the seeker a chance to bag two hiders for the price of one, we heard squeaky, sloshing footsteps step through the door. It was Thomas—the seeker. Shushing me with a finger over her own grinning lips, Charlie pulled me close, and held my arm while we waited for our certain doom. It was the first time I'd ever voluntarily been that close to a girl who wasn't my mom or grandma. We heard Thomas's shoes gingerly stepping in our direction, one squish after another. Charlie squeezed my arm tighter and I could feel the sting of each of her fingers digging in. She appeared to be trying to further hide herself behind my shoulder. I felt, deep down that I had to be brave—to show her how manly a seven-year-old I actually was. I sat up a little straighter and felt a warm swell of affection for Charlie rise in my chest. Then we heard Thomas stop. He asked one of the ladies from the kitchen, who'd stepped out from behind the counter with a clanking tray of cutlery, if she'd seen any kids come in. "No, can't say that I have," she said. Thomas bought it and bounded out the door into the roaring rain.

I exhaled. We were saved! But Charlie didn't let go of my arm.

I turned to look at her, secretly hoping she didn't want to let go, but curious as to why not all the same. She was smiling, almost laughing, and leaned in and pecked me on the cheek.

"Hmm," she said with a happy, but puzzled look on her face. "There's really nothing to that. They make it look so exciting on TV." Then, in a whirl of little girl giggles, she was gone, dashing off to her next hiding place.

Secretly, maybe even to me, she'd had my heart since that day. Even when things were good with Elle, it had always been Charlie's admiring glance that made my day.

After another dinner at the Haines' house, I finally worked up the courage to see where we stood once again.

We were sitting at the kitchen counter, alone.

"So," I said.

"So..." Charlie tucked her arms tightly around her middle.

"Have you had time to... think about things?" I asked, completely unnerved, thinking of how cool, or not, I was coming across.

Charlie grinned and unfolded her arms. "I think so."

"So...?"

She grinned again, and then burst into a laugh. "This is terrible."

I laughed, too. And then the laughter died down, and I was looking at my hands.

"So, what would you think if I started telling people that you and me are... going out?"

She leaned in close, smiled, and then pecked me on the cheek. "I think I'd be all right with that."

It all seemed like we had traveled back in time to that summer under the cafeteria table. I was so excited she agreed to be my girlfriend that I'm honestly not sure if I ran home, or flew. For the record, although I know for most people it would be a strange thing to say, I feel like I should let you know that I have not discovered that I *can* actually fly. But, if there was ever a night when I could've, it was that one.

I could tell from early on that, unlike my relationship with Elle, my relationship with Charlie would be far less focused on the physical nature of romance. Instead, we laughed a lot, talked a lot about our likes and dislikes—whether or not she liked chocolate better or vanilla, Coke or Pepsi, math or English, the Beatles or the Beach Boys, *Star Wars* or *Star Trek* (you know, all the important stuff)—and watched a lot of movies. Like, a lot of movies.

It didn't really matter what the movie was either. Whether it was something her dad wanted to watch—some old western, or a James Bond flick—or some made-for-TV low-budget extravaganza, we were in. We watched a lot of really stupid movies, too; you know, the ones that make you wonder if you just wasted two hours of your life. But I loved every minute I got to spend with Charlie.

Everything just felt right when I was with her, even down to the time we spent with her family. I had known them for a long time, like I've said before, but getting an inside look at their day-to-day life was showing me a glimpse of something I realized I was desperate for: a healthy, functional family.

Mr. and Mrs. Haines were very sweet and kind to each other. Even when they disagreed on something, they always seemed to resolve it in a very civil and reasonable way, or agreed to talk about it later. That was something I surely wasn't used to in my own house or anything I'd really seen up close before. Thomas's parents were very nice to me and seemed to get along just fine, but his dad worked a lot of long hours and traveled for his job pretty regularly, and I didn't see him and Mrs. Winters interact a lot. When I was hanging around the Haines house, I could sense that Coach adored his wife, and his kids, and that they loved him too. Knowing *that* was the kind of home

Charlie had been, and still was being, raised in made me attracted to her all the more.

I found myself looking forward to just being around her, not caring what we were doing or where we were. I just wanted to be with her. I seldom thought about my powers or gave them any use save for when they served me in getting to Charlie quicker by running to her house on the scarce country roads, or finishing the chores my mom gave me as fast as I was able so that I could leave and go be with my girlfriend. When I was with her, I suppressed any trace of superhuman-ness. I feared that her finding out would ruin what we had, though my ever-growing affection for her began to sprout in me an inkling of desire to tell her who I really was; that football, and the high school kid she thought she knew was only a portion of the entire picture. But, if I showed her what I was capable of and let her tell me what she really thought of it all, I would risk her seeing me as something different from what I was now, and I couldn't stand to think that things might not be that way forever. Of course, because of my sheer admiration of her (and desire to impress her and make her think I was cooler than I was), there were times I had almost just broken down and laid it all out. But then I would stop, recall Allie Rogers's house and think better of it.

Things were good.

I felt a sense of security, confidence, and joy that I had never realized were missing until that point in my life, and I couldn't come up with a reason compelling enough to give all of that away.

"So, I've got to tell you something," I said.

I was working up the courage to tell Thomas about Charlie and me. After the way things had gone with Elle, I was afraid he'd scold me for dating one of our closest friends and botching up that relationship too.

We had talked about plenty of girls throughout our friendship, and told each other about girls we thought we'd like to date or who was more attractive between two. We had definitely talked about Charlie before, asking what-ifs about what it would be like if one of us ever ended up with her, but those conversations never seemed to go much of anywhere because of our mutual friendship with her. We always agreed that Charlie was different from the other girls, and we liked it that way. But, because of that I'd never told him about any of my feelings for her. The subject just hadn't come up, and like most guys, we didn't really talk about things that could possibly make things uncomfortable between us.

But this was Thomas—my best friend.

I'd told him, and no one else, that I might be able to pass for Superman's forgotten younger brother, and then gave him proof! Compared to that, this was a piece of cake, right?

All of those thoughts were just simmering in the back of my mind as I waited to get my chance to deliver the news.

"What is it?" he asked.

"Well—"

"Actually, hold on," Thomas said. "I have some really big news."

"You do?"

Thomas smiled a somewhat embarrassed, but excited smile.

"Yeah," he said. "I think I'm going to ask Charlie to homecoming."

Thomas took the news about Charlie and me without batting an eye.

It was as if he had been planning to see a movie he was debating whether or not he really wanted to go see, and then found out at the ticket counter that it was sold out. A mild, double-checking, "Oh, really?" were his only words, followed by a thoughtful, "Hmm…"

I apologized, telling him the truth—that I'd had no idea he was planning to ask her to homecoming, or that he was interested in her at all. "Don't worry about it," he said. And then added, more emphatically, "Really, don't."

There was a pause that felt longer than it probably was, and then Thomas said, "That's awesome, man. I'm happy for you."

Then, for one of the few times I can remember in our friendship, we didn't have anything to talk about.

Thomas turned to go, stopped, turned back and appeared to have something to say. "I'll see you at practice."

And that was that.

Homecoming came late in the season that year—the weekend of our seventh game. We had only lost one game up to that point and were firmly in the lead in our district to make the state playoffs.

The entire Friday felt like a dream.

OHHS held its traditional pep rally to end the school day and Briggs whipped the crowd into a frenzy with a rousing speech as the football team stormed the basketball court. At the game, we pummeled the Durango Devils. By halftime I had already scored three touchdowns and we led 31-6. Coach Haines informed me in the locker room that Briggs was sitting me for the remainder of the game to try to keep me healthy for our postseason run. I laughed at the absurdity of it, but obliged and watched Thomas throw for two more scores in the second half. He didn't sit by me on the bench like he usually did, but he nodded in appreciation when I told him it was the best I'd ever seen him play, and said, "Thanks." I didn't want to push him. I knew he'd be okay after a few days.

When the time for the dance and all of its festivities rolled around on Saturday evening, I could hardly wait to see Charlie. Her parents were going to be chaperones at the dance, and so the three of them arrived at my mom's house to pick me up in Mrs. Haines's van, because Mrs. Haines wouldn't let Coach drive the truck to the dance. Charlie stepped out onto my front lawn in a long, elegant peach-colored dress (which I was told later was coral, but who can really tell) that made her look even more stunning than she normally did. Her hair was done up, and her eyes, cheeks and lips were accentuated with makeup I never really saw her wear that made her face look somehow soft and strong and confident and charming all at the same time. A silver bracelet hung from her dainty left wrist, perfectly matching the strappy high-heeled sandals that adorned her tiny feet. She was breathtaking. When she complimented my ensemble—a black shirt, black slacks, and a peach (or I guess, coral) tie—I almost felt embarrassed, like I was a peasant boy accompanying a princess to the royal ball. I shook hands with Coach Haines, who gave me a wink, while my mom greeted Charlie and her mom with hugs.

Collectively, the parents forced us to stand on the front lawn by some plants and a bush, and a big rock in the flower bed by the house, and pose for far too many awkward photos that made my face sore from smiling so much, before my mom told us to have fun and sent us on our way.

We ate dinner at the local Chili's while her parents went across the street to Subway, despite our insistence that we wouldn't mind if they ate with us. Kindly, they left us their credit card, and I tried to control my appetite. It's much easier to do that around a pretty girl in a fancy dress.

By the time we arrived at the high school for the dance, I already felt like we'd had a really fun night. Everything beyond would just be icing on the cake.

We walked in and quickly found Stacy and Rachel and their dates and talked to them for a while. Charlie complimented their dresses and hair, and they did the same, and told me I looked handsome. I saw Thomas on the other side of the gym with some cheerleader I knew he had no interest in, Zane and Caleb, and their dates. I really wanted to go over and say hello, but I didn't want to rub in the fact that I was at the dance with the girl he wanted to be there with, and decided to leave a meeting between us to chance. Just as I had made this decision, I felt a tap on my shoulder and turned to see Kiera Nash in a rather low-cut, short red spaghetti-strapped dress, with a tall, athletic guy I didn't recognize sporting a red shirt, black pants and a black tie.

"JJ, Charlie looks so pretty!" she said, as she leaned close to me. I could smell a hint of alcohol on her breath.

"Oh, thanks," I said, a bit unsure as to why she had come to talk to me.

Charlie turned from talking to Stacy and Rachel. "Oh, hi Kiera," she said. "Your dress is really fun!"

"Thank you so much," Kiera said. "Yours is lovely. And what about this guy?" She gestured toward me. "He cleans up pretty nice, huh?"

"Yes he does," Charlie said, looking at me with a smile. She turned back toward Kiera's date. "And who is this?"

"Oh, this is Nick," Kiera said, wrapping her arms around one of his. "He goes to Ferris State."

"Ferris?" I said, internally shocked, but trying to play it off coolly. "That's cool."

"How'd you guys meet?" Charlie chimed in.

"Oh," Kiera said, embarrassed as she looked toward him and pulled herself closer to him. "We met at a party."

Nick grinned.

"Oh yeah?" Charlie asked.

"Yeah," Nick said in his deep, college guy voice.

"All right, well it was nice seeing you guys," Kiera said after a moment. "C'mon babe." And together they walked off toward the dance floor.

"That was weird, right?" Charlie asked, as we watched them go.

"Uh, yes." I said without hesitation. We both laughed.

The night was nearly over by the time I finally got to slow dance with Charlie for the first time in my life. We'd been dancing to all the upbeat songs and talking to our friends and having a great time. I had already sweated through my shirt, but I was having a blast.

Homecoming with Elle had been fun, but there was something deeper with Charlie that felt vastly more satisfying. When she looked at me and our eyes met, it was like nothing else in the world mattered.

Holding her as we swayed to the lazy beat of the music felt like a perfect end to a wonderful night.

And that was when I remembered the poem I had written her during Thursday's test review in my Pre-Calc class. I had never been much of a poet, but I liked to write and we were studying *A Midsummer Night's Dream* in my English class, so I had decided to give it a try. I was pretty happy with what I'd come up with; something about moving mountains for her and never giving up on our love. You know, the basics.

In a flash, I'd convinced myself I wanted Charlie to read it right then, because it summed up exactly how I felt about her and I wanted her to know. It was in my locker, stuffed between pages about sine and cosine curves.

I told her I needed to go to the bathroom, and that I'd be right back and then excused myself, trying to hide my excitement as I walked through the throng of dancers gyrating to the booming rhythm of the next song that had come on.

The lights in the gymnasium were dimmed for the dance, and the unflattering fluorescent bulbs in the hallway had been completely turned off once the event had begun, so as not to distract from the festivities. I noticed that the gate they usually set up as a barrier to keep people from wandering the halls during those types of functions wasn't quite snug to the wall, making it even easier for me to quickly slip past and return it to its position. My locker was a straight shot down the hall from the doorway of the gymnasium.

So, once I'd gotten past the gate, I was about to take off at a dead sprint when I realized it was taking my eyes a few extra seconds to adjust. There was a remnant of bright in my vision that cut horizontally through the solid darkness before me. But as my eyes began to decipher the shapes of the lockers and even posters on the walls, I realized that what I was seeing wasn't a spot from a light, but actually a beam of light down the hall. It was coming from the boys' bathroom near the juniors' wing of the lockers. The door was closed most of the way—a strange realization when I thought about the way they were almost always propped open with a door jam.

As I moved closer to the light, the low musical thump of the gymnasium speakers faded away, and I heard a low voice, and then a shriek.

"Stop!" It was a girl's voice. There was a clattering sound and a metallic clank followed by a light thud. "Please," she said. It sounded like she might be crying, or on the verge, at least.

I hardly thought about it before I burst through the door, my eyes straining once again against the dramatic change in lighting. As they focused, I looked to the right and saw Kiera seated on the tile floor with her knees angled toward her chest, her hands braced on the floor for support, and her back against the wall near the two sinks in the room. Her hair was disheveled and her makeup was beginning to run from the dampness in her eyes. With a quiet gasp, her head turned toward me as I clambered into the room. Her gaze was pleading and terrified. An obviously empty silver flask laid on the ground. I looked from her to see her date, Nick—sleeves rolled up, tie loosened, shirt half untucked. He was breathing heavily and wiped his mouth with the back of his hand.

"Wrong door, man," he said, gesturing with the hand near his mouth. "This room's taken."

"What are you doing?" I asked.

"Just having some fun," he said.

"It doesn't look like everyone thinks so."

"Don't worry about it!"

"No," I said. "This—"

"I SAID DON'T WORRY ABOUT IT!"

He moved closer to me to try to scare me off, but I didn't move. I kept my eyes locked on his.

He raised his fists and grinned.

I stood my ground.

He lashed out with a wild right hook, but he didn't get near me.

Moving at about twice his speed, I opened the door of the nearest stall and slammed it into his oncoming fist with a sickening crack. Nick reeled back and cursed loudly, clutching his wrist just as the door from the hallway burst open again and Coach Haines, breathing hard, appeared around the corner with an intense, bewildered look in his eye.

"You broke my arm!" Nick shrieked, clutching his mangled forearm against his body. "God!" He fell to one knee.

For a moment, no one moved, save for our great heaving breaths. Coach Haines stopped, assessed the room, blinked once through his glasses, and then turned to me.

"Get her out of here."

Coach Haines returned his gaze to Nick and kept his eyes locked on the young man as I walked to Kiera, extended my hand and helped her from the floor. Her measured movements made her look like she was a statue that had come to life. I'm not sure why, but I wrapped my arm around her as we walked from the bathroom. She seemed like she needed to know that she was safe, and the gesture felt like the natural thing to do. She huddled close, burrowing into my side as we began to make our way down the long, dark hallway toward the swelling thunder of music coming from the gymnasium.

As we approached the gate that was now half-open from the several people who had been through it, Kiera stopped, looked at me, and then buried her wet face in my shirt, sobbing.

"Are you okay?" I asked, after a long moment, gripping her by the shoulders.

She shuttered, trying to stifle her emotions as she pulled herself away from me, and then spoke. "I don't know." She smiled, eyes glistening in the light shining toward us from the open door of the dance before fresh tears rolled down her cheeks. "Thank you," she said, and then her chin crinkled, and the sobs started again.

I scanned the crowd of dancers and spectators as we entered the gym. I spotted Ms. Henry standing over by the punch and veered us in her direction. As we passed by, I saw several students stop their movements and conversations, and gawk. *JJ and Kiera, together… again?!* I can only imagine how scandalous it looked. I spotted Thomas straining to see what was going on from about halfway across the room. But I thought of none of that as we made our way to Ms. Henry, who saw us approaching. Her expression flashed from joy to concern as she got a good look at Kiera's face.

Quickly, Ms. Henry strode forward and met Kiera with open arms. I watched as the two of them embraced and Kiera cried. People who were close enough to see Kiera looked on, concerned.

I watched too, unsure of what to do next. I felt a tug near my elbow on the fabric of my shirt. It was Charlie.

"What's going on?" she asked, shifting her eyes to Kiera, who was being escorted from the gym by Ms. Henry and another teacher.

"I need to get out of here," I said.

I did my best to explain to Charlie what had happened. She had, understandably, been a little confused by the appearance of Kiera and I walking into the gym, huddled together, but seemed to truly believe me when I told her what had happened.

"Why did you do it?" she'd asked.

I shrugged my shoulders, content to leave out any traces of evidence that might point to my secret.

"It just seemed like the thing I was supposed to do."

The night was all but ruined. After I retold my perspective of the events to Coach Haines, Principal Cook, and a police officer, Charlie's parents took me home.

As I was getting out of the car, Charlie squeezed my hand.

"You did the right thing."

43

The day after the dance was Sunday, and I was grateful not to have to be around anyone. I spent much of that day swimming in my own thoughts. I struggled to convince myself that I could find comfort in Charlie's words. For as much as I tried to think about anything else, I couldn't wipe Kiera's scared expression from my memory. *What if I hadn't been there? What if I had been there five minutes earlier?*

Although my abilities afforded me an advantage in many areas of life, they didn't help me fight my own thoughts.

I got a phone call from Mr. Vance, who was in the middle of transitioning into his new job with the Detroit Police Department, but was still working with the Oak Hill police to help establish the new police chief. He'd called to check in on me and hear my side of the story. But that only served to further bring the images of the previous night's events into vivid focus. When I finished telling him what had happened, he told me he was sorry that I'd had to experience it and assured me they were helping Kiera as much as they could.

As the day turned to dusk, I left my mom's house to get some fresh air in the cold October evening. I walked aimlessly with my hands in the pockets of my zip-up sweatshirt, unable to stop replaying the previous night's events in my mind.

The sun disappeared beyond the horizon, covering everything around me in a veil of gloomy grey light. I can't tell you how long it was before I found myself at the entrance of Henderson Field. *Football,* I thought. I was eager to play again—heck, even to practice—to get my mind off Kiera. I was dreading going back to school and having to talk to people less than twelve hours later.

I noticed that the gate was ajar slightly, and as I inspected the lock hanging from the chain that bound the metal doors together, I found that it wasn't latched. Everything was dark, and I took that as a sign that I was invited in, though I'm sure I could've found another way if I felt like jumping the fence. I strolled through the small atrium beneath the brick and stone grandstand bleachers. Slivers of moonlight spilled through small cracks and openings of the structure, reminding me that I really didn't know just how old the place was. The opening that led to the topside of the stands was highlighted in the soft light, and I gladly followed it and found a seat about twenty rows up near mid-field.

I sat and looked around, my warm breath drifting skyward in lazy visible tendrils. I thought about the game we had played that Friday, imagining some of the plays on the darkened field before me. I could almost hear the cheers and excitement, see the colors, feel the energy around me. But sports seemed like such a trivial thing to be thinking about.

How many more Kieras are out there, right now? I wondered. I had a hunch I didn't actually want to know the answer. Surely there was something I could do for some of them—a handful maybe—but what about the rest? What would happen to them? And why did things like that happen at all? I pictured myself bursting through the doors of more places, far seedier than a high school bathroom. How many comic books, or TV shows had I watched, or video games had I played where things like that happened? And never once had I realistically thought about myself being the one to step in and… save the day? Was that too weird to say? It felt like it. What was I even implying? That I ought to be doing that kind of stuff?

I came to my senses and realized that my fingers were nearly numb from the cold.

It was all crazy. All of it. I thought back to the night Thomas and I had tried to "fight crime" downtown. Absurd. *What could I possibly do by myself?*

I was getting sleepy. And for one of the few times I could recall since the previous Christmas, I felt exhausted.

I heard the whoop of a siren from somewhere toward the other side of town. With a groan, I stood.

I need to go home.

"JJ, what's wrong?"

Charlie had caught me in the middle of a deep train of thought, and snapped me back to reality in the coffee shop where we sat studying by the front window. An ambulance—sirens blaring, lights flashing over the dark streets—had raced by, sending my mind back to what I'd thought about a lot for the past few weeks: *Someone else is hurt. Someone else is in trouble.*

"It's nothing," I said. "I was just thinking."

"Yeah. And scowling."

"Oh," I said, trying to force my face to relax into a more pleasant expression. "Sorry."

"You don't have to be sorry," she said. "It's just that you haven't really been the same since…" She looked out the window, probably close to the way I had been doing so just moments before. "I'm starting to worry about you."

"Well," I started. I wanted to apologize again but thought better of it. "It's just… there's a lot going on."

She waited.

"What do you mean?" she asked.

"I just… I feel like I'm starting to see things differently."

"What things?"

"I don't know." I was trying to find the right words. "The world, I guess."

"Because of homecoming? You and Kiera?"

"Yeah," I said. Her face remained interested, but unreadable. I looked back out the window. "Well, no. Not like that. There's nothing going on with me and Kiera. I hope you know that."

Charlie grinned and picked up her coffee cup. "I know," she said. "That's not what I'm worried about. I'm worried about *you.* You don't seem happy. And it feels like you hardly even look at me when I'm around." She put her hand on my arm. "Before it seemed like every time I walked into a room you looked at me."

I realized I wasn't looking at her as she had said it.

"Before?"

Charlie laughed. "You think I didn't notice last year? Or freshman year? Or all of junior high?" We both laughed. "It just seems like you're distracted, and maybe dissatisfied with… your life."

"Yeah." What she said rang true somewhere deep down inside me. *Maybe I am. Maybe my life needs to be different from everyone else's.*

"JJ," she said. She looked concerned. "Are we breaking up?"

Wherever my mind was headed screeched to a halt in that moment. That was something I was not considering even a little bit. There were a lot of things I was unsure about, but the way I felt about that girl was not one of them.

But just telling her that wasn't enough.

"I'm not breaking up with you."

"You're not?" Charlie said, sounding both somewhat surprised and relieved. I glanced at the clock mounted on the wall—8:43 p.m.—and debated what to do next. *What the heck,* I thought. The coffee shop was going to close in seventeen minutes either way. I took the last drink of my—by that point—cold coffee, and then grinned at her.

"Do you trust me?"

Charlie and I stood near the fifty-yard-line of Henderson Field, on a bed of pristine green grass illuminated beneath the brilliant glow of the stadium lights. The tall privacy fence that had been installed the previous offseason to prevent "free loaders from not having to buy tickets," according to Briggs, hid us from view of the houses and anyone passing by on the surrounding streets.

I held a football that I'd taken from the burlap bag of gear in the bed of Coach Haines's truck, which had been entrusted to Charlie and me for the evening. The key to that truck had also been entrusted to us, which just so happened to share a key ring with the keys to the stadium and football facilities.

"Won't somebody wonder why the lights are on, on a Tuesday?" Charlie asked.

"Probably," I said. "But if anyone asks we'll just say it was maintenance."

"Okay, *smart guy,*" she said with a playful raise of her eyebrows. "What if the police show up?"

"Then we just run."

She laughed.

"It'll be fine."

"Okay, and remind me what we're doing here again?"

"Right," I said. I slapped the football with my free hand. "I've got to show you something."

"Show me something? On a football field? You realize I've seen every football game you've played here, right? I don't think you're going to do anything that will shock me."

I grinned.

"Well, what if I told you I want to show you something that only one other person in the world knows about?"

"And who is that?" I gave her a look that hinted that she already knew the answer. "Thomas?"

"Yes," I said, as I repeatedly tossed the ball over my head in an arc and caught it with the opposite hand. "Listen, Charlie…" I stopped throwing the ball and brought it to rest at my side. I was trying to find the right way to say it. "I can do things…" She looked at me squarely in the eyes, waiting.

"Like, what kinds of things?" she asked.

"Like, abnormal things; things no one else can do."

"Jay, are we talking about football? Because, I know you're good, but—"

"Not football. I'm a..." My mind went blank as I tried to think of what to call myself.

"Are you trying to tell me you're a... a vampire, or something?" She gave me a look that said that she was joking, but there was a hint of seriousness in her eyes.

"A vampire?" I laughed. "No, not a vampire."

"Well, what then?" she said after a moment.

"Just watch," I said.

I tossed her the ball, took off my jacket and got down into a sprinter's stance to make a show of the fact that I was about to run. After a breath, I catapulted from my curled position and broke into a full stride, bounding over the white lines at every five-yard increment on the field. Reaching the end zone in an instant I planted my left foot in the ground, turned right, and ran as hard as I could back toward Charlie, who stood unmoving where I'd started from. When I returned and halted next to her, she looked surprisingly unimpressed.

"Did you see that?" I said.

"What?"

"I ran."

"Yeah, that's good JJ. I don't want to be rude, but, you know I've seen you run before, right?"

"Yes," I chuckled. "But you haven't seen *that* before." I pointed over my shoulder toward the end zone I'd just returned from with my thumb.

"Am I missing something?" She looked confused.

"Charlie, I just ran to the end of the field and back."

"What?"

I nodded.

"No you didn't," she said. "I just watched you run down a few yards and then come back." Apparently from her angle, my showmanship had been a little lacking.

"Okay," I said, thinking of a way to help her understand. "Leave the ball here, and then let's walk down to the goal post down there."

She set the ball down in the dead center of the big painted letters that spelled "Oak Hill" in the middle of the field.

When we had reached the end zone, I positioned her to stand with her back against the goal post, and facing the fifty-yard-line.

"I'll be right back," I said.

Again, I turned and ran as hard as I could, the ground indenting beneath every footprint as I rocketed toward the ball in the middle of the field. As I reached it, I crouched, slid a hand under the cold brown football and brought it into the crook of my arm as I pivoted and began to make my way back to Charlie. When I arrived this time, I could see her eyes scrutinizing what she had just witnessed. They opened wide in disbelief when I dropped the ball in front of her feet.

"How did you…?" She looked past me, and then back at my face. "That's… That's…"

I smiled, waiting for her excitement. Instead, the look on her face turned to panic and suddenly I had a creeping sense of dread that maybe this hadn't been such a good idea.

Maybe I am a freak, I thought.

"Charlie," I said. I stepped toward.

"Wait," she said, putting her hands out in front of her, her palms facing me. "Just stay right there for a second."

"Charlie," I said.

"I just… I just… I need to sit down."

We walked over to the bleachers and were sitting a few rows up, looking at the illuminated field. Charlie hadn't said anything for what felt like an hour, but was probably closer to ten minutes. I couldn't think of anything to say.

"How long have you been like this?" she asked, finally breaking the silence.

"Pretty much since last Christmas," I said, as gently as I could manage.

"Christmas? What happened at Christmas?"

"Well, nothing really. I don't really know how it happened. I just woke up like this. But there were a few things that happened before."

"Like what?"

"Well, there was The Hit, the lockers, the basketball pole, the car and the snowplow, the—"

"Wait, the basketball pole?! That really *was* you?"

"Yeah," I said.

"I remember Marcus going on and on about that. I thought he'd just had too much to drink." We both laughed, and I could sense her relax.

"Is this real?" she asked.

"As far as I know."

"This is like a… a movie."

"Yeah," I said. "Honestly, I'm not really sure what to make of it."

"Wait a second," she said. "Football?"

I nodded. "Yeah. I've kind of been holding back, to tell the truth."

"Wow," she said. "Does my dad know?"

"I haven't told him. I haven't told anyone except…" I could feel the words welling up in my throat before I could fight the urge to say them. All of my secrets getting out into the open with the person I wanted to share them with the most felt like it was right in so many ways. But this felt hard. I looked down at my hands. "Listen," I exhaled. "Allie Rogers's house… That was me too."

I didn't want to look Charlie in the eyes for fear of what I might see.

"What do you mean?" she asked.

"I did it," I said. "It was me. I was the one who threw the tree."

"Well, hang on a second. My head is spinning a little bit here. Did you say 'threw' a tree?"

"Yeah," I said. "But it was an accident. I didn't know I could throw it that far."

"JJ, how far did you throw it?"

"Well, you know that barn, out by my grandparents' place?"

"Yeah," she said, slowly realizing what I was implying. "Wait… You're saying—"

"It wasn't from the barn. I was at the tree line across the field. It was the first day, and I… I didn't know that would happen." We were both quiet for a moment. "Hearing about Allie's house and her family at school was… well, that might be the worst I've ever felt about anything," I said. The tears had started to pool in my eyes. The last thing I wanted was for Charlie to see me cry. The thought of it was embarrassing. But, I couldn't stop the words from pouring out of my mouth, and I couldn't fight the emotions that came with them. "I've been terrified ever since. I'm afraid to do *anything* because then people will know. They'll see me as a freak, and they'll be afraid of me and then they'll send me away or something and run experiments on me, or kill me…"

There was a pause for several seconds where I could only hear the breeze rustling the trees in the nearby neighborhood. *Gosh,* I thought. *Now I've done it. She's got to think I'm an idiot, out here crying about all this.*

"It's cool and stuff," I said. "But, there's days I wish I could go back to just being normal, so I didn't have to deal with all of it."

More silence. I stared at the field.

But then I felt her hand on my arm. And then I felt her hair brush my cheek as she pulled herself close to me and wrapped herself in my arms, pressed to my chest.

"I don't think the world needs another normal guy," she said.

Knowing that Charlie *knew* gave me a sense of freedom I hadn't anticipated, but was grateful for.

Naturally, as the days went by and she'd had a chance to think about it more, she wanted to know more about why I was the way I was, and how it had happened. I told her what I knew, which wasn't much. I ventured guesses at the rest. At that point, the best I knew was that I had been born with some sort of abnormality. We'd learned about genetic mutations in biology, and that didn't seem like too much of a stretch. The theory that seemed to make the most sense was that my mom or dad had been unknowingly exposed to some kind of radiation before they had me. Beyond that guess, I knew nothing. But I was okay with it that way. I still wasn't ready to go to a doctor and open myself to the endless tests I figured they would want to try. Not knowing anything seemed to be the best way to keep everything in the dark.

45

I was getting dressed for football practice in the locker room later that week, thinking about going to Charlie's house later that night to watch a movie. Somehow things between us felt normal, even though it seemed like they shouldn't. But my thoughts were interrupted when I saw Thomas enter the room with Zane and Caleb.

The guys were laughing and carrying on about something that one of them had done over the previous weekend. I realized I had no idea what they were talking about; not even a little bit. As I thought more about it, it dawned on me that I hadn't really talked to Thomas for more than a couple of minutes at a time since I'd told him about me and Charlie—a span of nearly a month. My constant desire to be around Charlie left my time between school, football, and sleeping primarily spoken for—a detail that crept up on me slowly, and one that I had overlooked long before I realized it had happened. Thomas and I had said "hey" to each other in the parking lot before school, and been in several classes and football practice together, but I couldn't recall one time in that span that we had talked about anything of significance, and definitely nothing about Charlie.

I decided to broach the subject.

"Hey guys, what's up?" I said, sauntering up to them dressed only from the waist down.

Their laughter died down quickly. Thomas looked at me, and then turned to the others.

"I'll see you guys out there, okay?" Thomas clapped Caleb on the shoulder, walked past us and disappeared into the trainer's room down the hall.

"What's with him?" I asked.

"I don't know, man," Zane said. "He's been a little different the last little bit."

"What do you mean?"

"Well, he just..."

"Hasn't been hanging around you," Caleb interjected. His words struck me like a punch I wasn't ready for.

We made the playoffs with ease that year. But even though everyone knew we'd made the postseason nearly a month before the end of the season, that didn't diminish the fanfare that swept through the town.

It was Oak Hill's first appearance in the Michigan high school football postseason in over a decade, and we were "playing the best football this town has ever seen," according to Jimmy Dunham's playoff preview column in the *Oak Hill Press.* They were having a field day with the idea that the Acorns looked like they might be good enough to not just beat the Woodlake Warriors in the first round, but possibly go all the way. For the record, we were good enough, because I could make us as good as we needed to be.

Any local business that didn't normally display some kind of Acorns football support had happily jumped onto the bandwagon and wrote "Go Acorns!" or "Beat Woodlake!" on their big glowing marquees, or hung a sign in the front window, or hung a jersey on a wall somewhere in plain sight within their establishment.

We'd easily won our district, and the recruiting letters had started to pour in. It seemed like the rubber-banded stack of letters I found in my locker got larger every week.

Hacksaw was receiving mail by the truckload. Both Zane and Caleb were getting some serious attention as college-caliber offensive linemen because of all the yards I was racking up running through the "spacious gaps" they were creating. And even Thomas had gotten a couple of letters in the final weeks of the regular season.

Briggs was wound tighter than I had ever seen him. Pacing the field at practice, he barked tedious instructions to nearly everyone he saw, including Aaron, the athletic trainer. There were rumors he was being recruited by colleges too, and we all knew he would jump at the opportunity to coach at the next level.

"Cut with precision," he'd yelled at the running backs group during drills, jumping to the front of the line to passionately demonstrate what he meant. His breaths were forceful, and labored by the time he'd trotted back to where the rest of us stood. "I don't want to see... one more... lazy cut out here... from any of you... or so help me... I will kick your ass right here." He tossed the ball to the coach running the drill, and started off to turn his attention on some other group. "And get your damn knees up, Morris!" he said turning back to face us as he slowly back-pedaled away.

It's strange to play a team sport with a friend who won't talk to you.

Thomas and I had been on more teams together than I could remember, but I could only recall one other time that he had been mad at me in a way that affected sports—some controversy over a video game that led to Thomas sticking his gum to the brim of my hat, and then me wrestling him to the ground in the dugout at one of our baseball games.

But that was Little League, and this was varsity football—times in my life that seemed worlds apart from one another, especially when I considered the weightiness of the town's reaction to having a team in the playoffs, and the way that I had changed so much.

Everything had changed in the time that followed The Hit. People looked at me in a different way than they ever had before. Former players, and school alumni, and random Oak Hill citizens stopped me to say how much they appreciated me and were rooting for me, and couldn't wait to see me playing football on their TV someday. Those had always been fun moments. Those were the things

I had always daydreamed about during those Little League years.

In everyone else's minds, making the playoff was a sign of legitimacy, but at times, I couldn't help but wonder if their compliments, or hopes, or admiration, or whatever it was could even be considered valid. I hadn't earned them. I hadn't worked my whole life to hear those words, like Hacksaw or other guys who deserved it. I was just... lucky. I almost wanted to go back and tell them all it was all just a big trick, the way an older brother might explain a scary movie to a terrified sibling. *It's not real. It's all fake.*

But, I knew I couldn't do that. I didn't want to. Football was still the plan. It was the way out.

And so we were on our way to the playoffs and I was going to make sure we won the state championship whether Thomas talked to me or not. As long as he kept giving me the ball, there was nothing that could stop the Oak Hill Acorns.

46

Standing in the tunnel beneath the grandstands for a playoff game felt strangely different from the other nights I'd done the same thing. Even in our big games against Carrasco and other rival schools, there hadn't been quite as much energy from the crowd. Maybe it had to do with the idea that I finally felt like I was playing for something more meaningful than just winning a game. The playoffs were all about one thing—validation. All of the talk, all of the stats, all of the scouts, all of the letters, all of it had been well and good, but a chance in the playoffs was my shot to show exactly what I was made of, and that I deserved offers from the best schools in the country.

I jogged onto the pristine grass, glowing beneath the lights and blanketed by the noise of hundreds of cheering people donned in red and yellow. At the center of it all I stood in the midst of a throng of teenage boys wearing red jerseys with yellow numbers, and shiny helmets, beckoning the raucous crowd. I could see my breath escaping through the facemask of my helmet, illuminated against the dark sky, but the chills running up and down my skin had far less to do with the temperature than they did with the weight of the moment. I was confident in my own abilities, but I knew how much this game meant to my town.

It was going to be a big night.

It was nearing the end of the first quarter when I saw Thomas get thrown to the ground by one of the Woodlake linebackers after he'd handed me the ball. We were leading 7-3, but I'd already noticed three other similar instances through the first four possessions of the game.

The crowd was onto the Warriors' antagonistic aggressiveness, and booed wildly at every opportunity. But the referees seemed not to notice, or didn't care, and called penalties sparingly, which only made the fans all the more unhappy. Briggs was the closest to belligerent I'd ever seen him be and had nearly lost his voice with several minutes still to go in the first half. The Woodlake coaches appeared to be intensely calm and ignorant to any foul play on their team's part.

While I was defending our 21-10 lead early in the third quarter, a Woodlake receiver ran toward me to block on a running play. As I moved to get past him, I saw his eyes flick to the right of me. Something flashed in my peripheral and I turned just in time to see one of the Warriors' tight ends crouching into a dive in an attempt to take my knees out from under me. The receiver had just been a distraction. I felt anger well up in my chest as I realized their ill intent. I leapt just high enough to evade the tight end, and then, with one swipe of my left arm, flung the receiver toward his accomplice.

The play ended as Hacksaw wrestled the ball-carrier to the ground, but the fans were rising from their seats as I saw the referees huddled together near the Woodlake sideline. And then, about five yards from the receiver and tight end, who were clambering over one another trying to get up, I saw a yellow flag laying on the grass. *Finally,* I thought.

The referee who wore a white hat instead of the black caps the others had, the head referee, looked toward the press box and signaled a personal foul, unnecessary roughness call. Then he pointed toward our defense. The fans in the home stands were incredulous and roared in disapproval. The referee jogged toward me. "That's a warning, son." He blew a shrill blast from his whistle as he hustled back into position.

The anger boiled within me.

I took a deep breath to try to calm myself as we lined up for the next play. In a stroke of luck that had nothing to do with me, one of our defensive linemen forced a fumble that another one of our defenders recovered. We had the ball again, and I had every intention of scoring on this drive, and many more, to reprimand the Warriors for their meager and childish attempt to win a football game.

I had made up my mind. *Forget all of this sportsmanship stuff. I'm going to keep scoring until we're up by forty.* I was going to score on the next running play we called. Thomas kneeled in the middle of the huddle and rattled off the name of the play—a pass play.

"Why are we passing?" I yelled.

"It's the play, JJ," Thomas said.

"It's first down! Just give me the ball!"

"You got a problem with my play?" Thomas's voice rose to match mine. "Then why don't you go talk to Haines about it!"

"Guys, let's go," Zane said. "Clock's ticking."

"Yeah, leave your crap off the field," Josh chimed in.

"Fine," I said.

Thomas finished barking out everyone's assignments as we broke the huddle and then turned and grabbed a fistful of my jersey and pulled me toward him.

"We all know we're going to win this stupid thing, and your name's going to be all over the stupid news. Let someone else do one thing." He pushed me toward where I was supposed to be and then went to take his place behind the offensive line.

I settled into my stance, feeling the sting of my friend's words.

I was furious, heartbroken, and humiliated all at the same time.

Just do this.

The play started, and Thomas dropped back to pass. My job on that play was to swing out to the left side of the field as a last resort in case none of our other receivers were open. Thomas reared back and heaved the ball downfield. I watched the ball for a moment, but then my attention reflexively returned to Thomas and I saw two Woodlake linebackers approaching him from either side. It was the same thing that had been attempted on me just a few plays before, only this time it worked. I stood paralyzed as Thomas's body contorted between the two assailants.

That's it.

I didn't care about what Thomas had just said, or the fact that he was mad at me.

In three steps I was within arm's length of the first linebacker. I grabbed him by the back of his jersey as he tried to get up and shoved him back to the ground away from Thomas. The crowd's volume rose. I heard a commotion from the sidelines and whistles blowing from behind me. I saw the other linebacker nearly standing upright and grabbed him by the front of his jersey. I looked him square in the eyes, and then hurled him several yards away (although, that was with restraint, because I'd wanted to throw him through the field goal uprights). I stooped and offered my hand to Thomas who was sitting up, but still on the ground. He looked at me, and then stood on his own.

Soon referees were grabbing me and pulling me toward the Oak Hill sideline. The stands were teeming with cheering fans.

"Have a seat," Coach Haines said as I walked by him. "But, don't get comfortable."

The referees announced another personal foul, unnecessary roughness penalty and followed it by informing our sideline that I had been ejected from the game. The crowd erupted into vicious boos. Briggs was irate. Haines just looked over at me and gestured to the locker room.

My heart sank as I walked to the locker room with my helmet in my hand at my side.

How could I have been so stupid?!

I removed my jersey, and shoulder pads, and then took a seat on the bench in front of my locker. I was so mad, I didn't want to hear what was happening, but I couldn't keep myself from searching for a radio. After a few seconds of looking, I sat on the floor with my back against the cold concrete wall and listened to the noise of the crowd cyclically swell and fall silent. Eventually the sounds softened until they seemed to stop altogether. A marching band started playing, but it wasn't the Oak Hill fight song.

We lost the game 24-21.

Football season was over.

47

The town was quiet. Coach Haines and Charlie dropped me off at the driveway of my mom's house. We didn't talk much during the ride across town following our playoff loss.

I climbed out of the truck, shut the door, and then grabbed the red gym bag, with my number printed in yellow on its side, from the bed. I gave a half-hearted wave goodbye, and saw Coach Haines casually salute back, while Charlie blew me a kiss he couldn't see.

Turning to walk toward the house I froze. Before me sat a weathered maroon pickup truck. It was Hank's.

I saw a faint orange glow through the open driver's window, and then a puff of smoke billowing from within the truck.

"There he is," he said, as I walked up the driveway. He tapped the ash of his cigarette on the side of the truck and it fell a few paces from my feet. "I'm sorry about the game." He took another drag. "I guess you probably are too, huh?"

I couldn't stop looking at him. There was something that seemed so different about the way he was acting. I'd never seen him like this.

"Yeah," I said.

"The way you played this year, there isn't anybody in the state that can stop you… except you."

If you only knew, I thought. I forced a little chuckle to acknowledge his statement.

He opened the door and slid from his seat, his boots thudding on the pavement. He shut the door and leaned against it.

"You blew it tonight, kid," he said.

"I know."

"I know you do. But, you just made the road that much harder on yourself."

"The road?"

"Yeah. Scouts, coaches—they see that stuff, JJ." He held the cigarette to his lips and then blew out another steady stream of smoke. "If you want to play college ball, you're going to have to work your ass off from here on out."

We stood there looking at each other for a few moments. I shifted my weight, and adjusted the gym bag slung over my shoulder.

"You do *want* to play college football?" he said.

I shrugged.

It was the truth.

"At this second, I don't know."

Hank stuck the cigarette between his lips, while he turned and leaned into the truck. He reappeared with a stack of envelopes. "Well, then what the hell am I supposed to tell these guys?"

"What is that?"

"Ball State, Grand Valley, Eastern Michigan, Cincinnati, Indiana—Indiana, JJ! That's a Big Ten school. And they want you!" He dropped the glowing cigarette butt on the pavement and snuffed it out with his boot.

"Where did you get those?" I asked.

"These? Oh, this is just the beginning. I've been sending your tape out to—"

"Tape. What tape?"

"Your highlight tape. I made it. It's how you get noticed."

I was trying to stay calm. "Listen Hank, I appreciate it, but I don't need your help."

"Yes you do. After what I saw tonight, you *certainly* do now. If you want to reach your dream—"

"Hank—"

"Stop calling me that! I'm your dad."

I looked at the ground and sighed.

"If you're going to do this," he said. "Then you need me… JJ, you're good. You've got so much talent. Think about the possibilities. Money, fame, respect—isn't that what you've always wanted?"

I didn't know what to say back.

"And think about your family," he continued. "Think about your mom. You could give her everything."

"Please don't talk about her like you care."

"Hey! Watch it."

"I need to go."

"No, we're not finished."

"Yes we are." I dropped my bag by the garage and then headed back down the driveway toward the sidewalk.

"Don't do this, kid."

"Tell Mom I went to Thomas's." I turned and started down the road, away from my house.

"JJ!"

When I turned the corner and saw that no cars were on the street, I took off at full superpower speed. Even if Hank wanted to come after me, there was no way he'd catch up.

My mom didn't know that Thomas and I weren't exactly on speaking terms at that point. She hadn't asked about it, and I'd never brought it up.

I had no intention of going to the Winters' house. I pulled the collar of my jacket up and the brim of my baseball cap down with the hope that no one would recognize me.

A bright glow crested the top of a small hill on the road, and I slowed to a walk. The headlights appeared with blaring intensity, and then the vehicle swished past and faded into the night, leaving me walking down the shoulder of the pavement in darkness. It was a chilly night that straddled the line between fall and full-blown winter. I picked up my pace and began to jog, which for anyone else would've been an all-out sprint. Overhead, the stars shone bright between the looming treetops on either side of the road. I didn't see another car for the rest of the journey. Apparently, the citizens of Oak Hill were reeling from the abrupt ending of the football season. I tried not to think about it.

College football… is that what I'm supposed to do?

I couldn't stop thinking about the ideas Hank had mentioned. *Money, fame, respect…* I *did* want all of that. But I couldn't shake the feeling that something wasn't right about all of it. I mean football was great. I had loved every minute of it! And guys my age had probably dreamt of getting the opportunities I was getting a million times. But thinking down the path of the journey I was on, I couldn't help but wonder if it would all be enough. Especially after what had happened with Kiera, lots of money and pats on the back didn't seem like they would be worth all that much. For most people, professional sports was the biggest platform they'd ever have—the most influence they'd ever enjoy—and a lot of guys used their money to help people.

But, I'm not most people, I thought.

I arrived at Charlie's house and saw that the windows were all dark. I checked my watch. It was after midnight.

Creeping up the driveway, I arrived at the side of the house where Charlie's room was located on the second floor—the opposite corner from her parents' bedroom.

With two steps forward, I leapt onto the shingled roof that jutted out over the first story. I braced my landing with my hands, and guided myself onto the roof, nearly without any sound at all. I crawled the short, slanted distance to the window and softly knocked with one knuckle.

After a moment, a frazzled-looking Charlie appeared on the other side of the glass, tying the belt of her bathrobe around her waist. Quietly, she opened the window. There was no screen. I wasn't sure if I was supposed to climb in or not, so I just stayed sitting outside.

"JJ, what are you doing here?" she whispered.

"I'm sorry," I said. "I needed to not be at my house… Hank was there."

"Your dad?"

"Yeah."

"Well, if my parents hear us they're going to freak out."

"I know. I'm sorry." She seemed to relax a little and leaned on the window sill so that her head was almost all the way outside.

"Did you walk here?"

"Yeah."

"Oh my gosh! How long did that take?"

"Not that long actually. I ran part of it. Only took a few minutes."

"*A few minutes?* You need to get on the track team." She cracked a smile.

"Well, I might have to after the way that game ended tonight. Briggs is going to kill me."

"No, he won't," Charlie said. "He can't afford to."

"Well he told me he was going to kill me."

We both laughed as quietly as we could.

"Was your dad mad?" I asked.

"He seemed a little disappointed, but he'll get over it... I don't think he was mad at you. How was your dad?"

"I don't know," I said.

She laughed. "Is that bad?"

"I don't know. But, it was weirding me out."

She grinned as she reached out and gently took hold of my hand. Her skin was soft and warm.

"Charlie, can I ask you something?"

"Sure."

"Would you still like me if I wasn't on the football team?"

"Yeah. Of course I would."

"Okay. What about if I didn't have these... abilities?"

"Well, seeing as though I've only known about those for like two weeks now, I'd say you're probably safe. Why are you asking?"

"I don't know. I really like you, Charlie. Like, I might even love you. And that kind of scares me, because I don't really know where my life is going right now."

Charlie leaned farther out the window, took a handful of the front of my shirt and pulled me toward her. Then she closed her eyes and kissed me. Her lips felt like a warm fire against the damp coolness of my own.

After a moment she pulled away.

"Wherever you're going, I want to come too."

By January, the letters I'd once been so elated to see in my locker were becoming a pile of junk mail on my bedroom dresser. With increasing frequency Briggs would hand me a stack of white envelopes held together by a rubber band. He always seemed to make a point of doing this when there were at least a few other players around to marvel at his announcements of the programs included in that day's haul. "Illinois, Pittsburgh, and Wisconsin." "Looks like Nebraska finally joined the hunt." "Well, well, well… If it isn't the ol' Fightin' Irish." "What city is Virginia Tech in, anyway?" "Zane, don't you have family in Iowa? The Hawkeyes want JJ." "Penn State, Michigan, *and* Ohio State? That's quite a day, son."

I got phone calls nearly every day from the coaches from some of those schools. Some coaches had even visited Oak Hill High School and asked for me to be pulled out of class to talk to me.

I'd been invited to visit the campus for more than a dozen schools, although I'd only gone to three. The head coach walked me around and showed me all of their state-of-the-art facilities, and introduced me to players I'd seen on TV, and told me about the heritage and prestige of their football program before taking me and my mom out to a fancy dinner.

The year before, I would've been beyond excited to get to do any of it. But even though I was hearing from tons of schools in different states, the strongest pull was still in Michigan. Charlie was going to school at Wayne State University in Detroit to study to become a teacher, like her dad, and I knew it really didn't matter where I played, as long as I got a scholarship. I could reach the NFL from anywhere.

"So where do you think you'll go?" Charlie asked.

"I don't know. Probably Wayne State."

"Oh, come on. You can't go there just for me. U of M wants you!"

"So does everyone else."

"Yeah, but why not go to the biggest program around? We could still stay in touch, you know? Like we talked about."

"I know. I would just hate to be that far away from you most of the time."

"You'll be at practice every day, and probably all the big parties on the weekends, anyway. You wouldn't even see me. And besides Ann Arbor is less than an hour from Detroit."

"Charlie, don't say that. If you're an option, I am always going to pick you."

She grinned, then leaned close and kissed me. "I think I love you, JJ Morris."

It was hard to imagine a future without Charlie. I didn't want to play college football if it meant that I couldn't be with her, or move to a different city, or do anything unless she was going to be with me. We'd talked about careers—how she wanted to help kids get through school before settling down and raising a family, and how I had no idea what I would do outside of football. No matter how I felt about my long-term future, I was going to go to college for free, get my degree, and then think about the NFL. Charlie talked about it with wild excitement, as if her most fantastic dreams were waiting for her just down the road.

With almost as little effort as it takes to snap your fingers, I could make it all happen. Now that she knew what I really was, she knew that too. I tried to explain how I felt like an actor every time I stepped on the field. It wasn't real. None of it. It was all a facade, and it wasn't fair. Guys worked their whole lives to be where I was, and I hadn't done a thing.

"But, JJ," she would say. "You have a gift. Your story is different, because you are incredibly different. You have a chance to do things that most people can't even imagine. Why wouldn't you want to take advantage of that?"

She had a point.

"The Wolverines?" Briggs exclaimed in his office when I told him my plan to attend the University of Michigan. "Nobody around here ever even gets scouted by them."

"What happened to Michigan State?" Coach Haines said with a playful glance through his glasses. "You would've looked great in green."

We both laughed.

"I'm just kidding," he said. He hugged me. "Congratulations, kid. You've earned it."

I was glad Haines was there.

"Morris Picks U of M," was the headline of Jimmy Dunham's article that ran with a photo of me in a navy blue hat with a big block yellow "M" on the front, signing my letter of intent on National Signing Day. He went on to write that my signing was one of the best things to ever happen to Oak Hill, and then included a few quotes from Briggs talking about how raw I had been when I'd first started playing for him, but how proud he was of how far I'd come.

"The Wolverines are lucky to have him," he'd said.

I remember the pungent aroma of the Oak Hill High School weight room smelling like a year's worth of dirty socks. Between the sweat-soaked rubber mats, the grime of chalked, humid hands that clung to every weight and bar, and the mildew that wafted from the chronically leaky ceiling, "dirty socks" was probably a merciful comparison. The odor was far from pleasant, but had a certain haunting charm to it that's hard to forget. I have a lot of memories in that room.

When the weather finally began to turn warm after the bone-chilling cold of winter had subsided, instructors and coaches would often prop open the old black door of the weight room with a cinderblock. The door led directly outside to a parking lot, and they would place a box fan just inside the door frame to usher in the fresh, fragrant air of spring.

Although most years it was still well below fifty degrees at that point in the year, it was those days that hinted at the changing seasons and always made me realize how close we were to the end of the school year. For most other kids I knew my senior year, that was an exciting revelation, but for me, school had become equivalent with success and fun and freedom. Standing in front of the doorway fan, I was thinking about saying goodbye to OHHS for good. I was never going to be ready for it to be over. The future excited me, sure, but it also filled me with anxiety. Nothing beyond those hallways had ever been all that real, and suddenly it was hurtling toward me like a freight train. Despite all of my accomplishments, and even my superpowers, I was afraid.

Only Charlie would be my link to the familiar. Everything was going to change—my school, my living arrangements, my city, my friends, how much I saw my family—but not Charlie, and I was going to make sure of that.

"Have you seen Haines?" I asked Zane. He stood up from a squat rep, legs shaking, veins bulging from his temples, the weight and bar resting heavily across his meaty shoulders.

"Office," he grunted.

I was going to tell him my plan—my intentions with his daughter. *I know you think we're young,* I'd say. It was Coach. He'd understand.

My hand rested on the silver door handle as I thought about where to begin. This wasn't a conversation I'd really ever thought about up until the hour leading up to that moment.

I took a breath, turned the knob and walked in.

My pounding heart felt as though it turned to stone.

Coach Haines lay to the side of his desk with papers strewn about around him. He rested on his side, with one arm stretched in front of him and the other draped across his stomach as if he'd been struck. His glasses were askew on his face. From the corner of his mouth nearest the floor, I saw a glistening stream of red.

"Somebody call 9-1-1," I heard a voice say.

I realized it was mine.

Coach Haines had three months to a year to live—that's what the doctors said. It was advanced, it was getting worse, and there was little they could do.

Mrs. Haines's voice broke over the phone, and she cried as she delivered the news to me.

"I'm sorry," she said. "I'm sorry, JJ." I wanted to tell her to stop saying that—that she had nothing to apologize for—but there weren't any words I could think to offer. "He's resting now," she said. "They said they're going to keep him here for a few days."

"Oh," I said, forcing the sound from my mouth. I could feel a lump welling in the back of my throat, and coughed. "How's Charlie?"

"She's... well... she's not so great right now," Mrs. Haines said with the hint of a laugh. "I'll have her call you in a little while, after I finish letting some other people know."

"Okay." My house was quiet. My mom sat and read a magazine under the light by her rocking chair in the corner of our living room. On the other end of the phone, I could hear the hum of hospital noises between the soft sobs of Mrs. Haines.

"Mrs. Haines?"

"Yes?"

"Thanks for calling me."

"Of course, JJ," she said with surprise. "Coach is going to ask me if I did when he wakes up."

Charlie wasn't at school much over the next few weeks. Although she was still making an effort to talk to me after her dad's diagnosis, she seemed different, and distant. I'd only seen her three times: twice, briefly after school when she'd come to pick up her homework, and once at my mom's house when she came to "get away for a little while." Mostly, we talked on the phone at night. I couldn't remember the last time I'd seen her smile and she was uninterested in watching movies or really much of anything. A few times I tried to talk to her—to really talk to her—or get her to talk to me, but she would just hug me, leaving behind wet streaks on my T-shirt when she finally pulled away.

With the spring semester beginning its descent toward the last months of the school year, it seemed like everyone else's minds had turned to prom and final exams, but for me and Charlie, it felt like the world had stopped altogether, screeching to a violent halt in the midst of our fairy tale.

I felt utterly useless to the situation, and I hadn't gotten to talk to Coach much, to see for myself that he was, in fact, sick. I still didn't believe it, not all the way. Or at least I hadn't let it sink in. He seemed so normal. I mean there had been that time on the porch, but I hadn't thought much of it, and he didn't seem to either. Had he known?

Mrs. Haines answered when I called one day.

"Hold on," she said. "Let me get Charlie."

"No. I mean, yes, but can I ask you something?"

"Go ahead, sweetie," she said.

"Can I come over this weekend?"

"Oh, well… We're actually going out of town."

"Oh. Where?"

"Up to Colorado to see my mom."

"Oh, Charlie didn't say anything about it."

"Yeah, well, we've had the trip planned for quite a while. We were actually thinking of canceling it, but Bill—I mean, Coach—insisted that Charlie and I still go."

"You mean Coach is staying home?"

"Well, yeah. He said it would be okay. I'm worried about him, but he insisted. But, that's just him, you know?"

"Yeah…" It *was* like Coach to do something like send the people he loved away at the time anyone else would've demanded they alter their plans. "Do you think he'd mind if I still came over?"

"Oh, JJ," she said. "Would you? I don't know if he'd say it, but he would enjoy that, and honestly, it would make me feel better."

"Yes, of course."

"He doesn't want to be seen as a charity case, so—"

"Just tell him I don't have anyone to watch the game with."

Normally, when I walked into the Haines house, it smelled like laundry detergent, or some wonderful meal that Mrs. Haines was crafting in the kitchen, and or there'd be just a hint of Charlie's perfume to greet me at the door.

But that day, the air was stale and slightly warm, and there was a hint of something I can only describe as *hospital.* Perhaps it was the fact that I had been imagining him in a bed in a sterile white room, hooked up to machines and being tended to by nurses as I ran to the house, or maybe it was the picture stuck in my mind of him crumpled on the floor of his office. The idea of sickness was infecting my senses.

As I turned into the living room, I braced myself for what I might see: a worn and withered coach huddled beneath a blanket, with loose skin hanging from his cheeks and elbows, and a pile of bloody tissues on the coffee table.

But the sight that met me was actually quite normal.

Coach sat upright in his leather recliner, as he often did when he watched TV, with his slipper-covered feet propped up on the extended footrest. He wore a red Oak Hill T-shirt and grey sweatpants. Next to him on the end table, a silver can of Diet Coke gleamed alongside a half-empty fizzing glass in the changing light of the baseball game on the screen. One hand rested on the arm of the chair, with the other tucked behind his head—his elbow jutting out to the side. He wore one of the hats he coached in. He seemed just like the Coach Haines I always knew. The only difference I noticed was that the hair that normally peeked out from under the bill of his hat when he relaxed and pushed the cap back from his forehead was missing.

But before I could dwell on this detail, Coach spoke.

"JJ!" He turned slowly to look at me. "It's been a while. Nice shirt! Looks good on you."

I had forgotten I was wearing a Wolverines shirt. I laughed. "Thanks, Coach."

"Come on in, have a seat," he said. "Haven't missed much. We got a leadoff double, but they stranded two. No one's scored yet."

I took the seat on the couch where Charlie and I sat most often when we watched movies at the Haines' house.

"How's your mom?" Coach asked.

It was incredible to me that a guy with his life unraveling before his very eyes would be asking about somebody's mom. It didn't seem right.

"She's fine. I guess."

"You guess?"

"Well, yeah. I mean she is. I just…" I could lift farm equipment over my head and run faster than a speeding car, but this felt like it took all the strength I had. "How are *you*?" I guess, I was afraid of what I might hear.

But Coach just smiled with his kind eyes peering at me through his glasses.

"JJ," he said. "I've been better."

He laughed, and I felt a wave of calm wash away the nervousness I hadn't realized was causing my hands to coil into fists.

"Yeah," he said. "And I've learned that people say a lot of things that just make it worse." He chuckled again.

"Really?" I said. "Like what?"

"Well, just like when Mike—you know, Mike Vance—called a few days ago. And I love Mike. He and I have been friends for years. But he asked me what I was going to do. He said, 'Bill what are you going to do?' And I appreciate his concern, but how in this world am I supposed to answer that?"

"I don't know," I said. I started thinking back to asking him how he was doing, and started feeling rather sheepish. Of course he was doing terrible. It was a dumb question.

As if he could read my thoughts, he said, "But no matter what they say, having people that care about you never gets old." He sort of nodded in my direction when he said this, like he was gesturing to me being there. "I need people to care about me right now. But the truth is, I've always needed that. You just don't think about it until something like this happens. And the world needs that—people caring about other people, not being selfish, and not being so caught up in their own lives that they can see when someone needs help. And that's why *you're* a special kid, JJ. Because you know that." Somehow I felt proud and sad at the same time—staring a dying man in the eyes, listening to him talk about how he appreciated me.

"But, here's the last thing I am going to say on it, and then you have to promise me we'll just watch the game and not think about all of this, okay?"

I chuckled. "Okay."

"Today—right now—I'm alive. I don't know what will happen tomorrow, or how I'll feel, or what this vile disease will be doing in my body. But today, I have a gorgeous wife who loves me, a beautiful daughter who has a brilliant future ahead of her, I am surrounded by people who care about me and my family, and I am alive. Jay, I'm a lucky man."

Watching baseball with Coach Haines, Mrs. Haines, and Charlie became a regular part of my routine. I spent most of my nights with them that spring, watching the Tigers fledgling beginnings to their season and talking about their prospects of winning their division. We sat around and talked, and laughed, and watched games to the final out, even when Mrs. Haines would leave the room and return with a crumpled tissue and puffy eyes. Even when Coach Haines went to the hospital when they discovered that his kidneys were failing. Even when the doctors and nurses needed to talk to their patient and check his vitals. Even when Coach Haines slept through most of the games, and we turned the volume down so all you could hear was the steady beep of his heart rate monitor and the hum of medical machines.

It was almost two months exactly from the day of his diagnosis that Coach Haines fell asleep for good.

That sucked.

Everybody deals with pain in their own way. Some people eat. Some people drink. Some people go to church. Some people want to be alone and think.

I went to the barn.

After crashing through its roof sixteen months earlier, it was the first time I'd gone back. I stood before its folded form in the dark of the night. I could clearly see the mangled edges of the hole I had made when I'd misjudged my jump. So much had happened since that day. From the jubilation of discovering my superpowers, to the horror of realizing that I'd destroyed someone's house, to the exhilaration of success as a football player, to the wonder of dating Charlie, to the unsettling nature of saving Kiera, to the latest event—the heartache of death.

In my mind, no one would notice that a mutilated barn had been further mutilated.

Standing in the dark, the air was cool, but heavy and damp, fragrant with the smell of grass and new life. I took off my shirt and laid it next to my backpack near the road. I had come directly from the hospital, and I felt my chest tighten against the lump that was welling up into my throat. I leapt at the barn, and began swinging my fists at everything I could reach.

Wood splintered all around me with each cratering impact. I struck again. And again. I wanted my knuckles to hurt. I wanted them to bleed. I wanted to be able to see the pain I was feeling. But, after the initial swell of emotion, I looked down and saw that my knuckles were still perfectly intact. They felt like I had knocked firmly on someone's front door. That was all.

I began again, with more rage and fervor, each blow blasting shards of wood and metal, nails and shingles and hay, in every direction. I was working my way forward, striking whatever I could.

In the distance, probably close to a mile away, I saw a tiny rectangle of light appear. Immediately, I dropped to the ground, lying on my back, and surprised to feel mostly dirt beneath me. I had disturbed the peace. I wasn't thinking about the noise.

I heard nothing.

I held my hands in front of me again, just inches from my eyes, to be sure. A little dirty, but otherwise unmarked. Behind my fingers, I saw the stars.

Gazing into the multitude, I thought of Charlie, and then of God, and then of heaven, and then of Coach Haines.

I began to cry.

And I didn't stop for a long time.

I walked into Charlie's house the next day to find her sitting alone at their kitchen table. She hadn't gone to school, and it was well after the sun had set. A small pile of tissues sat next to her on the table, and she clung to a heather grey sweatshirt that was bundled in her arms. As I moved closer, I recognized it. It had been her dad's.

"JJ," she said, as if she was mildly startled by my presence.

"Hi," I said. She forced an unconvincing smile. "How ya' doing?" She looked down at the roll of clothing on her lap.

"It still smells like him," she said, with tears in her eyes.

I moved closer to wrap my arms around her.

But she put her hand on my chest, stopping me.

"JJ," she said. "Why did this happen?"

"I... I don't know."

And then she said the words that I don't think I'll ever forget.

"Wasn't there anything you could have done?"

What was I supposed to say?

"Couldn't you have saved him?" she continued.

"Saved him?"

"Couldn't they have used your blood?"

"I don't know. I'm not sure if—"

"Why didn't you try?"

"Try?"

"You're special, JJ. You could have done something."

"What could I do?"

She was crying now.

"Why didn't you do anything?"

"What could I—"

"Why, JJ?"

There was nothing I could think to say.

"If anyone," she sobbed, "could have… It was you."

I tried to hug her, to pull her close. This wasn't Charlie.

"Why didn't you do anything?!"

"Charlie?"

She was beating my chest with her closed fists.

"Why didn't you try?"

She struck harder, though I hardly felt it.

"Charlie?" Tears were forming in my own eyes and the lump in my throat was creeping back into position.

She fell limp in my arms, her final swings falling weakly until they stopped altogether.

Charlie had given up.

Coach Haines's funeral was held at the same church where he'd led my Sunday school class all those years before.

My mom and I got there just before the ceremony started. I hadn't heard from Charlie at all, though her mom had called to let us know about the viewing and everything. It was still just days after it all had happened, and I was reeling from the sudden changes in my life. None of that was helped by the sight of the ashy black casket, adorned with flowers, at the foot of the stage. There was a large photo of him next to it, mounted in a frame.

I slid into the second-to-last row. I'd told my mom a little bit about what had happened with Charlie, but I still didn't understand it all myself.

Several teachers and faculty from the high school spoke about how much of a stand-up guy Coach Haines was. They called him Bill. I always knew that was his name, but it felt foreign to hear people using it. They were talking about the man lying in the box, not the guy I knew.

Everything they said was very nice, but it was Principal Cook who said it best: "When Bill Haines told you you could do something, you felt like you actually could."

All I wanted was to talk to Coach Haines one more time. If I had the choice I would've given up anything to have that chance. But he was gone.

The preacher got up to talk and said some stuff about Jesus, and heaven, and eternity. He sprinkled in the word "legacy" and then talked about the way God had used Coach Haines in young people's lives.

God? I thought. *If God's real, then why didn't he do anything about this?*

"But sometimes, God lets things happen," he said, as if he could hear my thoughts. "He uses tragedies to get our attention, to give us a new perspective, to change us."

After the service, my mom and I hung around for the reception in the big room at the back of the church that was connected to the kitchen. We ate a few mints, and some au gratin potatoes, and talked to several people, and then we were getting ready to head for the door when Charlie's mom walked up to me.

"JJ, thank you so much for being here," she said. "I'm sorry about you and Charlie. She's having such a hard time with all of this."

"Oh, it's all right. I still wanted to come."

"Well, that means a lot," she said. "And, before you go, I wanted to make sure you got this." She produced a white envelope with the two letters of my name written on the back in Coach's scrawl. "He told me to make sure you got this."

I pulled the white envelope out of my pocket and placed it on the dresser in my room when I got home. I sat on my bed, looking at its upturned, crinkled corners from a few feet away.

Whatever was in there, I didn't feel like I was ready to see it. I stood and started to go pick it up. My hands were shaking.

"JJ," my mom called from the kitchen.

I came to my senses.

"Yeah mom?"

"Someone called for you."

I figured it was probably another college coach wanting to talk.

"Who was it?"

"Mr. Vance."

"Elle's dad?"

"Yeah. He said to call him back. He said he wants to talk."

If he was calling to console me about Coach, I didn't want to talk.

"Thanks Mom."

I didn't call him.

54

"So who are you taking to prom?" my mom asked a little over a week after the funeral. I think it was her way of trying to get my mind thinking about something happier. Honestly, I'd forgotten all about the dance.

"You're sure Charlie won't go?"

"Mom," I said. "I told you, Charlie said she needs a break."

"I know," she said. "But this is your senior prom, and you guys really should go together."

"I didn't even talk to her at the funeral. There's no way we're going to go to a dance together."

She looked a little taken aback, but then nodded her head slightly.

"I get it, buddy boy," she said in the way she always did when she knew I was sad. "And I won't make you go. I just think it would be good to have a night where you can just be a high school kid again. Not so grown up and having to deal with this kind of stuff."

She hugged me.

"You'll always be my baby," she said.

I didn't mind.

"I know, Mom."

At school, everyone from the students to the teachers to the janitors and the lunchroom staff were dejected to varying degrees.

Coach Haines had been a friend to nearly everyone he met. His rough-around-the-edges demeanor served him well as a coach, but masked a kind heart, and a willingness to help.

To some of us, he had been more than a friend. A mentor. An advisor. A father figure. An advocate. A protector.

But to Charlie, he hadn't just been one of those things, he'd been all of them. She wasn't at school. With final exams just a few weeks away, I wondered if she'd even bother coming back before then. Part of me didn't blame her at all, while the other part was desperate to talk to her and try to make things right.

People knew Coach and I spent a lot of time together. So, from the moment I was back at school, I hardly ever talked to anyone who didn't bring him up or ask me about the whole situation. I could only imagine what that would have been like for Charlie.

A finger lightly tapped me on the shoulder in my journalism class. I had zoned out, sitting at my desk. The classroom buzzed with quiet conversation as students talked through the projects they were working on in small groups. One group was working on a tribute article to Coach Haines. Another was writing a piece that talked about a special patch the football team would wear on their jerseys in his honor the following year. It dawned on me that I wouldn't be wearing one the following year. The thought was always there, but hit me hard in that moment.

I remembered the tap on the shoulder.

Turning around, I found myself looking into the concerned eyes of Kiera Nash. Those eyes—the same ones I had seen in the bathroom, tear-filled, and surrounded by streaky makeup. This time around, her eyes were clear and focused. They were plain. They were kind.

"Are you okay?" she whispered.

"Yeah," I said. "I think so." She offered a sympathetic smile. I appreciated the gesture, although, to be honest, I was tired of people asking me that question. I started to turn back around in my chair, when I heard her inhale like she was about to say something.

"Look," she said, speaking at an even lower volume than before.

"I know this is hard. And... I know... I know we aren't really friends, but you did kind of save my life. I just want you to know that if you want to talk about it..."

I kept waiting for her to bat her eyelashes or give me some sort of knowing glance, but she didn't. Kiera was serious.

"Thanks."

I was in the weight room after school, but not because I was lifting.

I was thinking about Coach. Just being around the place he normally would've been felt comforting somehow.

I wondered what Charlie was doing and if she was still mad at me. And somehow, I couldn't stop my mind from wandering back to Kiera. When had she become so nice?

I was sitting on one of the benches when Hacksaw came in, music screeching from his headphones. He didn't realize I was there until he was a good five steps through the door. When he did, our eyes met for an instant and I saw his body slightly convulse from the surprise, before he recovered and kept walking like nothing had happened.

A few moments later, after I had returned to my thoughts, I was again interrupted when I heard Hacksaw's groans that were probably far louder than he intended because of the deafening tones pumping straight into his head as he bench-pressed a would-be impressive amount of weight.

He pumped out a few more reps as I watched, the muscles in his arms bulging as they strained against the burden.

Finally, with one last exhausted grunt, he re-racked the weights. He lay there, arms over his head, with his chest heaving.

And what was that on his face? I assumed he was sweating a lot, but was he crying? The mighty Hacksaw, crying over his triumph?

"You all right man?" I asked loudly.

Nothing.

"Are you all right?!" I yelled.

Still no sign that he'd heard me.

I walked (faster than I meant to) over to where a spotter would normally stand and leaned over the bar.

"ARE YOU ALL RIGHT?"

Startled by my sudden appearance over him, Hacksaw scrambled to an upright position, and then whipped around as he tore his headphones from his ears.

"What the hell, man?!" he said.

"What? I'm sorry. I just saw that you were..." I made a vague gesture, trying not to let him know what I'd seen.

He coughed and then wiped his face with a towel.

"I'm fine man," he said. He seemed stern and threatening.

"Okay, I didn't mean to..." I just stood there. I was literally at a loss for what I was supposed to do next. Leave? Try to make a joke? Act like none of this had happened?

He stood and started to walk out of the room.

"You wouldn't get it anyway," he said. "You can go anywhere you want."

"What do you mean?"

He stopped and turned around, like he was about to unload the deepest secret of his life.

"Forget it," he said. He turned toward the door.

"Marcus," I said. I think it was the first time I'd ever called him by his real name to his face. "I don't know what's going on, but I'm sorry."

He whipped around.

"You're sorry?" He stepped toward me. "Oh, thank you for walking around here, being better than everyone else, and getting offers, and getting your name in the paper, and taking my spot on this stupid team. And now telling me you're sorry! Listen Morris, I don't need you to feel sorry for me!"

"Wait," I said. "I'm not trying to... What do you mean taking your spot?"

He shook his head, like he was debating with himself.

"This was supposed to be my team." He was looking off at one of the walls in the weight room. "When I moved here from Texas, this was going to be my second chance—my fresh start."

"Wait, wasn't your team in Texas good though?"

"Yeah," he said. "Too good. I was on the team, but I didn't really get to play. My dad hated it. He was embarrassed of me."

"Oh," I said.

"When we moved for his job, this was going to be my shot. I grew a little. I was stronger than I'd ever been. I felt great. But it wasn't good enough."

"Dude, you are good," I said.

Hacksaw's eyes bored into my own. "Well, I thought I was... until I met you."

My heart sank. I was a cheat. A phony. And here was a kid who worked his butt off, and by all accounts should have been the star of his school, and he was being overshadowed by a fake.

"Listen, I'm not good. I'm just... lucky," I said.

"Call it whatever you want. You're the one that the newspapers and the colleges want to talk to. You're the one my dad tells people about."

"You have letters," I said. "You've got plenty of offers, don't you?"

"Not the right one." Hacksaw looked off toward the wall.

"The right one?"

"The University of Texas was the only one that mattered to my old man. He played there."

"Oh," I said.

"So... Listen... I don't know if I want to stand here and talk about all this with the guy who probably got offered by my school and is dating my ex-girlfriend."

"Oh, right," I said. "Well, I haven't heard from Texas. And about Charlie... we're not really..."

"What?"

"After Coach, you know? She just… I don't really know what happened."

"Oh," he said.

We both sat in silence for a moment.

"I'm sorry," he said.

55

It was a few weeks later that I was sitting on my couch in my sweats one night, watching *Teen Wolf* with my mom. Although our opportunities to do stuff like that were becoming increasingly more infrequent, it wasn't completely out of the ordinary for us. But, that night was different. It was the night of prom.

My mom hadn't been thrilled that I wasn't going to the dance. In fact, she was sure that I'd regret it. But even though we went back and forth, and I'd explained the fact that I didn't feel right about going with anyone other than Charlie like a dozen times, it wasn't until I told her I wanted to watch a movie with her that she mellowed a bit.

"You'll be my date," I'd said. "Who needs a dance?"

"Well, I'll agree to it on one condition," she said.

"What's that?"

"Call Mr. Vance. He called again and left a message for you."

"Oh, did he?"

"Did you ever call him back the last time, JJ?" She said my name in the way only moms can say it.

"Well..."

She gave me a stern look that only moms can give.

"I'll call him back," I said. "Tomorrow."

Her seriousness gave way to an eye roll, and she gave me one of those I'm-letting-you-off-the-hook grins.

We were settled in, twenty minutes into the film, and two-thirds of the way through our second tub of popcorn when we heard a knock at the door.

My mom and I looked at each other before she got up to answer the door.

After a moment she moved from the entryway, and started back toward the couch.

"It's for you."

I walked to the door, unsure of who would be paying me an unannounced visit at this time on this night.

"Hi. Sorry to bug you." It was Kiera.

I was completely taken off guard.

"Kiera?" I said. "What are you doing here? Aren't you supposed to be at prom?"

"I could ask you the same thing," she said with a chuckle. "But, you know, I've kind of lost my pizazz for dances."

"Yeah, I guess I could imagine that."

She smiled.

"Anyway," she said. "This isn't supposed to be anything weird. I know your mom's here. I just thought you could use a friend tonight."

I leaned back to look at my mom from behind the door.

She shrugged in what I perceived to be an approving way.

"Come on in."

So, Kiera and my mom sat on our couch, and I sat on the floor while we finished *Teen Wolf*, and then *Raiders of the Lost Ark* because Kiera had never seen it. After we finished the second of our double feature, my mom made pancakes.

By the time we finished our breakfast it was nearly midnight.

"Well, I'd better go," Kiera said. She stood and began to put on her jacket.

My mom picked up the syrup streaked plates and nodded in Kiera's direction.

"I'll finish cleaning up," she said.

After Kiera thanked my mom for the food, and for letting her spend the evening with us, I opened the front door and we walked to her car, parked on the street in front of our house.

"Thanks for coming over," I said.

"Sorry I didn't call before."

"Oh, it's fine. Really. Thank you. It was great."

"Well," she said, and she looked down at her feet. "I'm really sorry for everything that happened the last time we hung out."

"It's okay," I said. "We were younger and dumber back then."

She looked up at me and laughed.

"Well, just know that I'm sorry," she said.

"Okay," I said as our chuckling died down, and I started to think about what she'd said. "Why?"

"I don't know. You just deserve better."

"Well, I don't know about that," I muttered.

"You do." Her eyes were intent on mine. "JJ, you're one of the good ones."

She smiled, climbed into her car, and drove off into the night, leaving me standing in the middle of the street.

The orange paper crinkled, and then flitted and tumbled through the air like a floating feather, before hitting the linoleum floor of the high school hallway and sliding about three feet toward the lockers on the opposite wall. I would have sworn I hadn't touched the bulletin board as I passed. Classes were in session, so I was the only person roaming the empty halls.

Deciding to be a good person and throw it away, I stopped to pick up the paper. But, as I went to ball it up and toss it in the trash can, I got a glimpse of the bold black letters on the front of the page: BATTLE OF THE BANDS! THIS FRIDAY, MAY 10!

It was hard for me to fully grasp the fact that I was looking at a flyer for an event that would happen after I had graduated from high school. Graduation was Thursday night. I would be a free man in less than seventy-two hours.

As I stood, reading the rest of the advertisement about how awesome the event was going to be, I became aware of the pitter-patter of footsteps about to round the corner to where I was. I turned and looked to see Kiera with her backpack slung over her shoulders and both arms carrying two textbooks. Apparently I startled her, as she saw me and took a frenzied step backward.

"Oh, JJ," she said. "Were you trying to give me a heart attack?"

"Sorry," I said. We both laughed. "I heard you coming."

"What's that?" she asked, nodding toward the orange paper.

"It's some Battle of the Bands thing."

"Are you going?" she asked.

"I don't know. I didn't even know about it until about two

minutes ago."

"Well, you should think about it. I'll be there. Jenny's dating Dylan now so I guess we're going to see his band."

"Jenny's dating Dylan?"

"Yeah, she's always had a thing for singers."

"Hm..."

"Well, it would probably suck less for me if you were there. Jenny's kind of annoying. Besides, I don't know how many more times we're going to get to hang out before you head off to get famous."

"Yeah," I said. I knew she was making a joke, but the truth of it settled over me. How many more times was I going to get to see her, or anyone else? Was that a good thing? "I'll think about it."

"Well, I've got to get to class," she said. "Let me know if you're going to go."

She walked away, and disappeared around the corner.

In a few days my life is going to change, I thought. I had thought so much about graduating and being out on my own that I hadn't realized everything that I was never going to experience again. Of course I wanted to stay in touch with my friends, but would I? And what about my mom? If I moved to a whole different city how often would I even get to see her? And what about my secret? I mean, I knew I was nearly indestructible, but how would I survive out there in the world?

I heard a rustling behind me and turned to see a flurry of orange papers skittering across the floor.

"Well, crap."

It was Thomas.

In one arm he held a messy stack of the orange flyers, and in his other hand a single sheet.

I raced over, knowing I didn't have to slow my walk or movements in front of him. I scooped up the papers from the floor and offered them back to him in a fraction of a second.

He looked at the papers and then into my eyes with a blank

expression.

I saw his eyebrow quiver upward as his mouth broke into a grin.

"Showoff," he said.

We both laughed, and I felt a sense of relief wash over me I didn't know I needed.

"What's up, man?" I said.

"Not a lot. Just trying to put up these posters."

"Why?"

"Because I'm going to be there."

"Why?"

"Because I'm in a band now."

"You are?" I almost burst out laughing. I had never known Thomas to do anything musical.

"Shut up."

"What? What do you play? What band are you in?"

"I'm in The Tommy Guns with Dylan and them. I play the drums."

"The drums?"

"Yeah, I'm… learning."

He laughed.

"I know it's kind of ridiculous, but it's fun."

"No, that's cool," I said. "You always just struck me as more of a stand-in-the-back-and-make-fun-of-the-band kind of guy."

"That's fair," he said with a chuckle. "I guess that'll just have to be you now."

"I guess so."

"So, are you coming then?"

I thought back to Kiera.

"Yeah… I don't know yet." I looked down the hall toward the direction Kiera had gone. "Maybe."

"Is Charlie…?" he started. "I mean, well… Look man… About all of that… I don't know, I'm sorry."

"Oh, it's okay," I said. "We'll see what happens, I guess."

"No," he said. "I mean… About her coming between you and me. I was frustrated. I guess I still am a little bit, but that was stupid."

It was like a weight was lifted off of my shoulders. I just wanted to hug him, but obviously we were too cool for that.

"No worries, man. I understand."

He smiled a little half smile that let me know he was glad to have that out of the way.

"And, while we're being real for a minute," he added. "I'm sorry about Coach too. I know that probably really sucked for you, man. It sucked for me, and I know you talked to him a lot more than I ever did."

I can't tell you exactly what it was that made me think of it, but when Thomas said those words, like a bolt of lightning striking my brain, I suddenly remembered that on my dresser in my room at home sat a sealed white envelope with my name written in Coach's handwriting.

"He told me to make sure you got this," Mrs. Haines had said.

I began to open the envelope as soon as I had closed the door to my room. I didn't know what I would find, but only that they were the final words I would ever have from Coach.

Initially, I was sliding my finger along the glued fold of the envelope, neatly unsticking it from itself. But a mixture of excitement and impatience caused me to move a bit too quickly, and the envelope began to tear. Throwing my caution aside, I tore it open the rest of the way and then eagerly peered inside.

I saw a single, crisp white sheet of paper, folded in thirds.

Carefully, I removed the paper from what was left of its packaging and unfolded it, the page loudly crackling in the quietness of my room.

I read:

JJ,

I know these last few weeks have probably been hard on you. But, I wanted to say thank you for caring for me and my family so well through this difficult time.

You are an amazing kid, who is growing up to be an amazing man. I'm proud to have met you.

And, I know that you're talented and you have the ability to do things other people can't even dream of, and that's probably what most people will celebrate about you. But, most of the world will never know your mightiest gift: your love for other people.

I'm ashamed to say it took me much longer to learn that trait for myself. My destiny was far different than I ever expected, and far better than I could have hoped for.

Life is more than wins and losses.

Take care my friend.

Signed,
Blackjack Bill Haines

58

I could hear the screeches and swells of sound booming from guitar amps before I ever walked through the doors of the Oak Hill auditorium.

Nestled between the gymnasium and classroom wings of the school, the auditorium was a room I had walked past nearly every day for four years, but entered just over a dozen times.

The stage was illuminated with bright white bulbs that had yellowed with age, casting the band that was preparing to play in warm tones. The drummer nervously fidgeted with his sticks as he looked back and forth between his other two bandmates. The bass player stood hunched and statue-like, his long hair hiding his face and neck. The guitar player strummed out a few more fuzzy sounding chords from his glossy black instrument, and then summoned to the crowd of an optimistic estimate of about fifty students that had gathered excitedly around the edge of the stage.

The rest of the room was sparsely inhabited with staff members who were chaperoning the event and a few students who sat in the cushioned theater seats, though it was hard to see where anyone was because of the lights of the stage that contrasted with the dark walls of the room. The seats were divided into two sections separated by a center aisle along the sloping floor that led back to where I stood near the entryway.

As I surveyed the Battle of the Bands, I couldn't help but wonder if it was the last time I'd step foot in this place.

My life had been full of those kinds of thoughts for well over a month, and I was beginning to recognize them as a bit on the overly sentimental side, though that didn't seem to stop me from thinking them.

It felt weird to be at Oak Hill High School and no longer be a student there. Walking across the stage they'd set up on the football field for the graduation ceremony had been the last official act of my high school career. But that wasn't the most interesting part of that day.

After the ceremony ended, I was talking with my mom and my grandparents when a tap on the shoulder caused me to turn around and see Charlie standing in her red cap and gown with a gold tassel on her hat and a matching cord hanging over her shoulders.

I had seen her at school for final exams the weeks prior, but that was the first time she'd approached me since the night at her house.

"Congratulations," she'd said as she leaned in and hugged me.

"You too." There was something familiar and surreal about the smell of her hair and the feel of her wrapped in my arms.

She pulled herself away from me but remained touching both of my arms, keeping us face to face.

"Listen," she began. "I'm sorry... about everything. I know it wasn't fair to you—what I said. And... I just..." She was starting to tear up. "I just don't want to move on without at least trying to figure this out. It's just with everything that's been going on, I don't know how I feel. But, I'm trying JJ. I'm trying."

I was still thinking about that moment, even though it was days later, as I stood in the middle of the auditorium at the Battle of the Bands. But my thoughts were cut short when I saw the outline of a teenage girl approaching me.

"You made it!" Kiera said, stepping close enough that I could see her face in the dim light. She was beaming.

"Yeah," I said. "I thought about what you said, how this might be the last time we're all together. I didn't want to miss it."

She grinned.

"Good," she said. She took my hand and led me to the throng of students near the stage. She looked me in the eyes, then released my hand and turned toward the stage, putting her arms up above her head as she danced and swayed to the rhythm of the song.

The band, despite a few squeaks and sour notes, wasn't all that bad, and I actually enjoyed listening to their deafening punk rock. Occasionally during the set, I would catch Kiera gazing at me, and I couldn't help but smile.

A final long chord rang out as the drummer speedily hit every drum and cymbal he had, and the student crowd clapped and wooed their approval. The musicians took a bow and then began to exit the stage.

Doubled over, with a pair of drumsticks protruding from the back pocket of his jeans, I saw Thomas dragging a rug with a different drum set on it and putting it in position in the deep center of the stage.

"This should be… entertaining," I said to Kiera.

She laughed.

"Hey," she said. "There's a bonfire after this. A few people are going to be there. Do you want to go?"

"A bonfire?"

"Yeah," she said. "And let me rephrase that. Do you want to go with me?"

I could feel my cheeks flush.

"Are you asking me out?"

She grinned.

"Maybe."

As flattered as I was, and as much as I had come to appreciate Kiera, I knew what I had to do.

"Well," I started. I looked toward the back of the room as if I could find the right words written on the back wall. And just as my eyes focused through the darkness, the back doors opened and a rush of fluorescent light poured in, momentarily disrupting the aesthetic of the room, and illuminating its culprit—Charlie.

Charlie's eyes swept the auditorium. She stood on her toes trying to look at every possible inch of the scene before her. She spotted me and began walking in my direction.

"Could you hold on for one second?" I asked Kiera.

She nodded.

I walked, as normal of a speed as I could manage, to meet Charlie in the center walkway that split the room.

"JJ," she said as she saw me. "Your mom told me you'd be here."

"What's up?" I asked.

"I wanted to see you."

"You did?"

She hugged me. "I miss hanging out with you," she said.

"I miss it, too."

She pulled away from me, smiling, and looked me in the eyes. "Well, let's get out of here," she said. "Let's go watch a movie or something, like old times."

Old times, I thought. *That's what all of this is.*

"JJ," Kiera said. She was walking up the aisle toward us, gesturing to the stage. "They're starting!"

Charlie eyed her warily.

"JJ?" Charlie asked.

"We are the Tommy Guns," Dylan's amplified voice bellowed. "This is a new song called 'Stampede'... Two! Three! Four!"

I heard Thomas start playing the snare in a fast, pulsing rhythm, as low guitar sounds swelled in behind him.

"JJ?" Kiera said.

I looked back and forth between Kiera and Charlie, their eyes both looking expectantly into mine.

But my choice was already made.

It had been made long before I'd ever realized it.

I turned to Kiera.

"I'm sorry," I said.

And then I turned toward Charlie.

"Do you trust me?" I asked.

Slowly, she nodded.

I leaned in and kissed her cheek.

"Nothing to it," I said.

She smiled as I walked past her toward the back door.

The music crescendoed to a deafening roar and the band crashed into a swaggering rock-n-roll groove just as I burst through the doors of the auditorium into the hallway.

By the time the girls would have reached the same spot, I was already gone.

I ran out into the night, headed for the future.

In the corner of the small screen that sat before me was a small black rectangle with the date and time stamped in white numbers and letters. The time was counted in military style and showed the seconds ticking away rhythmically. Although the finer details of the silent black-and-white image were a little blurry, I could make out the outline of a man wearing a dark hooded jacket walking up to a convenience store counter where another man waited behind the register.

After a verbal exchange, the hooded figure raised a pump-action shotgun and cocked it—the barrel aimed at the man behind the counter, who raised his hands.

The verbal exchange continued, with the cashier shaking his head or nodding at the questions until the hooded man turned to look at an apparent noise.

I could just make out what looked like a car steering wheel attached to a small box slide into the frame near the hooded figure's feet. As his head moved down to inspect the object, a dark blur entered from the same direction the steering wheel came from, moving so fast it could hardly be captured on film.

In an instant, the hooded figure flew onto the counter seemingly unconscious (or worse) from what appeared to be an invisible explosion. For an instant I saw a third man standing near the counter, but he quickly disappeared and the hooded man's shotgun fell to the floor, the barrel of the weapon severely bent.

Bewildered, the man behind the counter put his hands on his head as he looked around the room, and then the image froze.

"So, was that the steering column of the getaway car?" Detroit

Police Captain Mike Vance asked from behind the large wooden desk in the room, gesturing to the laptop screen in front of me.

I nodded. "Yeah, I had to make sure his buddy didn't get away."

Mike broke out into a hearty laugh.

"That was my favorite part," he said. But quickly, his laugh died down and his tone turned more grave. "But, JJ, you know you've got to be more careful. If this video were to get into civilian hands, or worse, if the media got ahold of it, it would go viral within the day, and we'd probably both wind up in trouble."

"I know," I said. "I'm sorry, sir. I forgot to check for cameras before I went in."

"You don't have to 'Sir,' me JJ—not when it's just the two of us like this."

"Sorry."

"Well, don't worry too much about this one. I was able to get all of the security footage from that place. And honestly, you did great. This kind of stuff is exactly why I wanted you. I just can't wait until I can get you on the bigger stuff."

"And when will that be, if you don't mind me asking?"

"Well, when you get a little more settled in. The last thing I need is a guy I vouched for destroying half the city trying to take down all of the drug lords in one day."

We both laughed.

"Once you get up to speed on who's out there, all of our policies and procedures, and generally, just how to be a cop, then we can kick it up a notch."

"But, I thought I wasn't a cop."

"Well, technically you're my intern. So, no, you're not a cop, but you need to know what a cop knows so you know what not to do, or at least, just know if you are doing the wrong thing."

When I finally called Mike back, nearing my high school graduation, we met for coffee and he laid out the case he had been building on me. It had nothing to do with me dumping his daughter. After witnessing my athletic abilities, my appetite, and the way I had gotten onto the roof of the building across from the bar that night with Thomas, he knew there was something different about me. When he did some further digging, and started "paying attention" as he put it, he started noticing other things. He had been back in town to finish up some police business in Oak Hill when Coach Haines and the on-duty police officer had relayed the story of me running into the bathroom and disarming an assailant at homecoming. They all knew I had no training, and should have been scared for my life. Mike's suspicions were all but confirmed. Once he started to put the pieces together, he remembered the Rogers' house.

"Trees don't just appear in a place they're not supposed to unless there's a tornado," he'd told me. "You were the tornado."

He had me dead to rights.

I shrugged. "I mean... yeah."

I waited to see if anyone was going to barge into the coffee shop, or if the guy sitting by the window across the room would suddenly charge me with his gun drawn and handcuffs ready. But none of that happened.

Instead, Mike was sitting with his hands resting on the table and looking at me.

"You know, I've seen a lot of things and I've heard about a lot more," he said. He turned and looked around, and then lowered his voice. "But, this is the craziest thing I've ever heard."

He laughed, and shook his head in disbelief.

"What are you going to do, JJ?"

"Do? You mean, you're not going to... arrest me?"

"Arrest you?" he whispered, stifling a chuckle. "I don't think I could if I wanted to. And for the record, I don't."

"Really?" I said. "But, what about the tree and everything?"

"Well," he said. "I don't honestly believe you did it on purpose. No one was seriously hurt. And I talked to Allie's dad. He said their insurance covered everything. We'll call it a failed experiment."

I sat back in my chair, and breathed a sigh of deep relief. It felt like I'd crossed into some new territory I hadn't experienced before, something like freedom.

"So back to my question," he said. "What are you going to do?"

"Well..." I didn't know how to say it. "My plan had been football. But lately, I've wondered if I'm like this for something different... something bigger."

"Hmm..." he said. He sat back in his chair and looked out the window of the coffee shop. "Well, I don't really know how it would work, but I've been named a captain in the Detroit Police Department. That means I can hire people, or at least make a case to get an intern. Maybe we can figure out a way to use your—erm—'gifts,' to help people. I might even be able to get DPD to help pay for some school if you're interested. Wayne State has a good program."

Of course, Briggs and my dad hadn't been happy when I broke the news to them that I wouldn't be playing college football.

"You're throwing your life away," Briggs had bellowed, slamming his palm on his desk, and knocking over a stack of recruiting letters.

My dad, who had been leaning against the wall shaking his head, suddenly stood up straight and looked at the coach.

"Let's go, JJ," he said.

In the hallway of the locker room, in which we had both kept lockers, he pulled me aside.

"JJ, you do what you need to do. I used to believe in something, too—something bigger than all of this. You go chase it. And don't you ever let it go."

He hugged me. And I hugged him back.

Surprisingly, my mom was relieved that I wasn't playing football. But, she was anxious about me moving.

"Detroit?" she asked. "But it's so dangerous there. And everything's old and broken down."

"I know, mom. I'll be fine. I'll come back to visit as often as I can."

"I know you will, baby. It's just that you're growing up so fast."

I laughed. "I know, Mom."

She hugged me in the way that only moms can.

"Mom," I said. "I love you."

I didn't tell Kiera. I just said goodbye, hoping she'd forget about me and eventually find a good guy to live a safe, normal life with. More than anything, I just wanted her to be happy.

Thomas was the only one who knew everything.

"So, you're going to be like Batman?" he said.

"Kind of." I laughed. "We'll see, I guess."

"But, what about a name? You don't have a cool name."

"I'll work on that."

"Well, what are you going to tell people about football?"

"I don't know."

We both sat in silence for a moment.

"Steroids," Thomas finally said.

"What?"

"Yeah, I'll just start spreading rumors that you got in trouble for steroids. It's the only explanation."

I laughed. "Thanks."

I thought about all of that, and all of those people, a lot during the first few months in Detroit.

I still do.

I was thinking about them as I got up to leave Mike's office.

"JJ," he said. "I know we've talked about this some, but I feel like I need to warn you that this isn't going to be a glamorous job. Fame and fortune and spandex probably aren't in the cards. You're going to see stuff—deal with things that will keep you up at night. You're going to see the very worst that humanity has to offer. But, there are going to be people who survive because of you. There are going to be victims who receive justice, and bad guys who think twice before they act in evil because of you. There are going to be parents and grandparents, and brother and sisters, and cousins and friends who will breathe a little easier when they send their loved ones off to school, or work, or out to have fun, just because they know you're around. And there will be little boys and girls who see what you're doing, and you will inspire them to be heroic and have courage, and to be an advocate for others. Son, you're going to make a difference in this world."

His words felt like they filled up the room, and my heart felt like it ballooned in my chest.

"I hope so," I said.

I sighed, and then turned to reach for the door handle. I still had to go get my stuff from my apartment before class that afternoon, and then my date with Charlie.

"Oh, one more thing," Mike said.

I faced him again.

"I'm going to need some sort of alias for you—a code name we can use to help keep JJ Morris disassociated from the antics of this superhero who'll be running around town."

I tried to keep my emotions bottled, but couldn't hide a slight grin at the word "superhero." And then I thought about the question.

"A name?" I asked.

He nodded.

"How about Blackjack?"

AFTERWORD

He stands in the street observing.

Smoke pours from the windows of a house, billowing in tilted columns toward the night sky. This is someone's home, or it used to be. Though the flames are hidden from view, the flickering orange light tells the ominous tale. It's a tragedy.

On the front lawn, a woman cries, her arms wrapped around two small children. She pulls them away from the sweltering hotness, toward the street. They scream and writhe against her protection. They are yelling something—a word. It's the same word over and over again, desperation leaping from their tongues.

A name.

Someone is still inside.

The man in the street, unrelated to the others—a mere passerby—realizes the full situation now.

He has a choice to make.

He's already chosen.

Long ago, he dreamt of destiny, and legacy, and meaning, and purpose, though he didn't know their names.

He looks around and sees that everything is marred by evil and destruction. The world has gone bad. Maybe it's always been that way.

Regardless, he is compelled to do something.

Right now, he knows that he must do something.

And he knows that this one act, this one offering, is only a drop in the bucket—and it might cost him everything he has.

But, he's already made his decision.

He hasn't chosen to be a hero, but that's what they'll call him if he succeeds.

He seeks to do right, to make a difference, to change the world.

Is he me? Is he someone more qualified? Is he someone with the right equipment to do this task? Is he a teenager? Is he a woman? Is he just someone who saw an opportunity to do something?

Is he you?

For me, the fight begins anew each morning. The pressure to give in or give up is ever present, and my resolve never seems as strong as it was when I first began.

But still, I fight.

I punch and claw and struggle and run and jump, and do whatever is required to be free of the chains that would so willingly tether me to my own comfort. Those are the chains of selfishness.

I fight because I must.

I fight because I know there are some who can't. The strong must defend the weak, and I am strong. And so I fight the devil I see in the mirror, because what he wants doesn't help anyone else. What he wants is for no one but him. And that's not something I could live with, waking up one day when I'm old and grey and saying I never thought of anyone else.

No, I was meant for more.

So here we are. You've read my story. You know my beginnings. Am I special? Am I a hero? Am I even real? Am I just a work of someone's imagination? Does it matter?

Somewhere, there's a house on fire, now, as I take the time to write these words. I am uniquely gifted to do something about that.

Maybe your skin isn't fireproof like mine.

Maybe you can't break through walls like I can.

Maybe you don't run faster than cars like I do.

My gifts are my own.

And so are yours.

We are all uniquely gifted to do something.

But our uniqueness isn't the reason for our existence.

It's how we use it that matters.

There are people struggling. People who need rescue, or a friend, or hope. People I can help. People only you can help. And they are not alone.

We might not change the world. But we might change the world for one.

We must find the one.

And the next one.

And the next.

We must fight.

We must.

Because the fire rages on.

ACKNOWLEDGMENTS

If you're ever going to try to write a book in your spare time there are a few things you should know. It takes a lot of time, a lot of late nights (or early mornings), a lot of sitting and staring blankly out of windows, a lot of saying no to other things you'd rather be doing, a lot of cups of coffee, and a lot of talking to other people about your ideas. If you're lucky, that last item is what makes the whole project go. There will be days that you, the author, the one who's supposed to be the most excited about your idea, are sick of even thinking about it and the last thing you want to do is actually sit down and work on the thing. That's when a well-timed "How's your book coming?" or "I can't wait to read it," is like a shot of creative adrenaline straight into your veins. Yes, you need the drive, the know-how, and the elbow grease to get it done, just like everyone says, but what you really need — what you nearly cannot do without — is a community who loves you, and supports you, and cheers you on, and wants to see you accomplish your goals.

I have been fortunate enough to have one.

First, I have to thank my wife, Brianna. I always say that she's my toughest critic, but through this entire endeavor she has been my biggest encouragement. At times when I felt like I didn't want to sit down to write, or even was unsure if I wanted to continue on with the whole process, she was the one who picked me up, brushed me off, told me she loved me and that I should get to work. And I can't even begin to imagine all of the instances where I asked if I could bounce an idea off of her, or asked her to tell me something a second or third time because I had been distracted with a thought for this book. She has been a trooper, a cheerleader, and the biggest influence in me actually doing this and chasing my dream. Also, she is the one who designed the cover, and mapped the entire interior of this work, down to the very words you are reading now. She's smart, she's beautiful, and she's a talented artist. I'm humbled to be her husband. I love you babe!

My family has played a crucial role in all of this as well. From the time I was in elementary school, my parents have always encouraged my writing and my desire to tell stories. I am fortunate to have parents who instilled in me a value of hard work, integrity, a value for family, and a love for people, who did their best to lead me toward success while nurturing my natural interests. Thank you from the very bottom of my heart Mom and Dad. And speaking of mom and dad, my in-laws have been nothing short of instrumental in my writing career. Rick and Janelle are some of the most kind, and generous people I have the pleasure of having in my life, and they have brought me into their family like one of their own children. They care about the things I care about, they get excited about the things I am excited about, and they have been so wonderful through the process of me working on this project that I really don't think I have the time or space to say all the things I'd like to. Thank you Rick and Janelle.

The original idea for this story came from my relationship with my wife's brothers, Eric and Ryan. When I first started toying around with writing a book, it was because I wanted to write something for them that would encourage them as they grew into adulthood. But, that was when they were both still in high school, and now here we are years later and they're both well on their way to being successful, valued contributors to our society and are probably smarter and wiser than I can hope to be. Sorry I missed my window, but I'm glad you guys turned out all right.

To the rest of my family—Ashley, Ben, Whitney, Brett, Grandma and Grandpa Coffey, and Grandma and Grandpa Willis – thank you for asking me about the book, being excited with me, and cheering me on from many miles away. I love you all!

I have a great group of friends who really don't care about writing books, but they seem to like me pretty well. Somehow they have put up with me talking about writing a book for over two years now, and are all still acting like they're interested and that they still want to be my friends. Nathan, Sarah, Chuck, Christie, Courtney, Josh, Jordan, Amanda, Eli, and Erin, you guys are great! I promise I'll stop talking about books... until I start writing the next one.

Thank you Zach Rady and Rocco Napoli for letting me pick your brains about life as high schoolers and for inspiring Thomas and JJ's friendship. You guys breathed life into this story and helped me stay motivated to continue writing it for all the other Zachs and Roccos out there.

To all of my beta readers—Ronny Barrier, Andrew Cauthron, Erin Contreras, Ben Murphy, Tiffany Ravedutti, Nathan Southard, and Ethan Speights—thank you for your honest (but gentle) feedback. You helped me color within the lines and make this story more vibrant than I ever could have alone.

I'd especially like to thank Yancey Arrington—my authorial co-conspirator. His encouragement of my skillset has been more beneficial for my confidence as a writer than that of anyone else in my adult life. He has affirmed me in my gifting time and again, and consistently helped keep me accountable to the writing I had committed to. Yancey, thank you so much for all those days we stood around and talked about books and writing and navigating the world of ISBN numbers and author pages! Mostly, thank you for your encouragement and your friendship.

To my editor, Diane Krause, thank you so much for your kindness to me and your brilliant work in helping me complete the journey of this project. I am utterly grateful for your willingness to work on *Super*.

And finally, thank you to Tom Harkema—the real life Coach Haines. I had already moved away from our small town when he was diagnosed with cancer, and since then I've been sad I never really got to say goodbye. I had learned about leadership and caring about people, but Coach Harkema was a picture of it I got to see almost every day during my four years of high school. Coach Harkema taught me that the best coaching doesn't happen on the playing field. For all the small moments when you asked me how I was, or consoled me after a girl broke my heart, or told me how proud you were of me, or challenged me to be better than I thought I could be, thank you Coach.

ABOUT THE AUTHOR

Jon Coffey is a writer, storyteller, and sports enthusiast. He grew up in the lower peninsula of Michigan before moving to Texas in his early 20s. He holds a Bachelor of Arts degree in journalism from Michigan State University.

Jon works full-time as a content writer and editor for Clear Creek Community Church, a non-denominational church located near Houston. He currently resides in League City, Texas with his wife Brianna and their dog, Piper.

Made in the
USA
Lexington, KY